10-00
EAR

- 6 APR 2016

STAR
PUB

Tarla Dalal

—India's #1 Cookery Author—

Delicious
DIABETIC
RECIPES

Low Calorie Cooking

S&C

SANJAY & CO.

MUMBAI

Other Books by Tarla Dalal

INDIAN COOKING
Tava Cooking
Rotis & Subzis
Desi Khana
The Complete Gujarati Cookbook
Mithai
Chaat
Achaar aur Parathe
The Rajasthani Cookbook **New**

GENERAL COOKING
Exciting Vegetarian Cooking
Party Cooking
Microwave Cooking
Quick & Easy Vegetarian Cooking
Saatvik Khana
Mixer Cookbook
The Pleasures of Vegetarian Cooking
The Delights of Vegetarian Cooking
The Joys of Vegetarian Cooking
Cooking with Kids
Snacks Under 10 Minutes

WESTERN COOKING
The Complete Italian Cookbook
The Chocolate Cookbook
Eggless Desserts
Mocktails & Snacks
Soups & Salads
Mexican Cooking
Easy Gourmet Cooking

TOTAL HEALTH
Low Calorie Healthy Cooking
Pregnancy Cookbook
Baby and Toddler Cookbook **New**
Cooking with 1 Teaspoon of Oil **New**
Home Remedies **New**

MINI SERIES
A New World of Idlis & Dosas
Cooking under Ten Minutes
Pizzas and Pasta
Fun Food for Children
Roz ka Khana
Microwave - Desi Khana
T.V. Meals **New**

641.5638   dB 10/10/05

Recipe Research & Production Design	**Nutritionist** Nisha Elchiwala	**Marketing Consultant** Harvinder Bindra, Addvalue International	**Photography** Sandeep Mhatre	**Design** Satyamangal Rege
Pinky Dixit Arati Fedane Jyoti Jain			**Food Stylist** Saba Gaziyani	**Printed by** Jupiter Prints, Mumbai

Price Rs. 250/-

Copyright© Sanjay & Co.
ISBN No. 81-86469-69-9

Published & distributed by
SANJAY & COMPANY
353 / A-1, Shah & Nahar Industrial Estate,
Dhanraj Mill Compound, Lower Parel (W),
Mumbai 400 013. INDIA.
Tel: (91-22) 496 8068 / Fax: (91-22) 496 5876
Email: sanjay@tarladalal.com / Website: www.tarladalal.com

DISCLAMIER
While every precaution has been taken in the preparation of this book, the publishers and the authors assume no responsibility for errors or omissions. Neither is any liability assumed for damages resulting from the use of information contained herein. And of course, no book is a substitute for a qualified medical advice. Also, different people react to same treatment in different ways. So it is wiser to consult your doctor or nutritionist before making any changes in your daily living pattern.

BULK PURCHASES: Tarla Dalal Cookbooks are ideal gifts. If you are interested in buying more than 500 assorted copies of Tarla Dalal Cookbooks at special prices, please contact us at 91-22-496 8068 or email sanjay@tarladalal.com.

Foreward

There are about 50 million diabetics in India today according to a survey by the World Health Organization (WHO). This study reveals that a large number of Indians are predisposed to diabetes.

Diabetes is a lifelong condition that can be managed with careful diet control and proper medication (either oral medication or insulin) under your physician's supervision. Dietary modification is an important aspect in the management of diabetes. In fact there is no substitute for good diet control. The success of any therapy for diabetes depends on the eating habits of that individual. **What you eat and when you eat is extremely important**. So some modifications in eating habits are very helpful for every individual with diabetes. But at times, most diabetics get frustrated with the monotonous 'diabetic diet' prescribed and the long list of foods that one has to avoid. And that is exactly the right time to refer to this book.

This book gives lucid information on some basic facts about diabetes as well as diabetic diet for lay people. It is a collection of meticulously planned recipes from different cuisines like Indian, Continental, Italian, Chinese and Mexican to add more variety to your meals. All the recipes are scientifically planned and nutritionally balanced. They will definitely enable you to enjoy your meals without compromising on dietary principles. Another advantage is that all the dishes are those that your family can enjoy with you.

Nutritive values are given along with each recipe including its carbohydrate and fat content. Some other interesting features of this book worth mentioning are practical cooking tips, charts and diabetic menus for handy reference.

I am sure that these recipes will enable every diabetic to enjoy his meals and yet keep a check on calories, fat and carbohydrates. So, the next time someone says that a diabetic diet is boring and uninteresting, tell him or her to refer to this book. I am sure they will be just as surprised, as I was when I first saw the index of this delightful collection of DELICIOUS DIABETIC RECIPES.

With Best Wishes

R B Phatak

Dr. R B Phatak (MD)
Diabetologist

Introduction

Dear Friends,

When a person is diagnosed to have diabetes, initially there is a lot of panic and shock, both for the person diagnosed and the family. Once this initial, yet natural panic is dealt with, it's important to learn more about the nature of the illness and all that's involved in coming to terms with it.

If one has a family history of diabetes, diet control and exercise can delay its onset. These preventive measures will ensure that you live a healthier and fuller life long after you are diagnosed to have diabetes.

A diabetic person must also learn more about the ailment itself, as well as how to maintain a healthy lifestyle and acceptable blood sugar levels. Both medical and dietetic advice is extremely beneficial and for this reason I am grateful to **Dr. R. B. Phatak, an eminent diabetologist**, who has helped us with invaluable information on the subject. He has selflessly shared his time and experiences with us, without which this book may have appeared incomplete.

Inspite of not being a medical person myself, over the years I have been inundated with umpteen requests to plan diabetic menus or suggest diabetic recipes for friends who themselves are diabetic or their loved ones are.

I have received warm letters, concerned e - mails and frantic phone calls on our helpline saying, "It's rakhi tomorrow and my brother is diabetic, what sugarless mithai can I make for him?". Such queries set me thinking and I began by modifying an old recipe of malai peda using artificial sweetener instead of sugar. After this, friends and family encouraged me to create more recipes that are good for diabetics to eat and most importantly ones that do not look like 'patient food'.

Later, I sat down with my research team and nutritionist and we gave the matter a lot of serious thought. "Necessity is the mother of invention", they say and that need made me look for ways to tempt the diabetic palate and add more flavour to these dishes without adding unnecessary calories.

Hypocrates, the father of medicine (460 - 357 BC), said 'Nature cures'. He advocated "Your food shall be your medicine" and this book is based on these maxims. I have chosen and adapted delicious recipes from various cuisines of the world to pamper the palate as well as help in controlling diabetes. Mouthwatering delicacies have been reworked to make them more suitable for the diabetic person.

Ingredients like karela and methi may not sound interesting at all, but if they are cooked in a manner that makes them retain most of their nutritive values and also tempt your palate, then my job is well accomplished. Try the recipes just once and I assure you that you and your family will enjoy them. If a new diet is planned around the normal dietary pattern of the family/person, it will enable the person to accept it more easily and keep your family healthy.

My team of nutritionists has carefully analysed each recipe to ensure that it is absolutely safe for diabetics and that all the required nutrients are present in the correct amounts. We have also added a food exchange list that will allow a lot of flexibility in the diet and also make allowances for occasional indulgences... undoubtedly, in small quantities...

Index

Recipe Index

Indian Flavours

International Flavours

Basic Recipes

Sample Diabetic Menu Plans

About Diabetes

Diabetes is a condition that is characterized by high blood sugar (glucose) in our body.

Under normal conditions the food we eat is broken down into **glucose**, which is a simple **sugar,** that leads to a rise in our blood sugar levels which is also referred to as blood glucose levels. As both terms refer to the same condition, we have referred to it as **blood sugar levels** throughout this book.

After meals a hormone called **insulin,** secreted by the **beta cells** of the pancreas, decreases the blood sugar levels and aids in producing energy for our body cells. Without enough insulin, glucose from the food that is consumed builds up in the blood stream, initiating various health problems.

Lack of insulin or its insufficient production leads to a rise in the blood sugar levels which is commonly known as <u>Diabetes Mellitus.</u>

Causes of Diabetes

How diabetes develops is not really known, but the most common causes are **genetics (heredity), obesity, irregular and unhealthy eating habits and stress.**

Genetics (heredity) plays an important role in the manifestation of diabetes. If one has a family history of diabetes, then it is wisest to take all the possible precautionary measures beginning from childhood to lay a strong foundation to delay its onset or to even avoid it.

Many people are prone to developing diabetes, especially after the age of 30 years. Hence, it is advisable to have regular meals, indulge in an exercise programme and restrict the consumption of junk foods and alcohol to delay the onset of diabetes.

Obesity. Most obese individuals are prone to developing diabetes as excessive fat stores can interfere with the body's ability to utilize insulin effectively and in turn lead to high blood sugar levels. People who have high fat deposits on their abdomen (apple shaped obesity) have a higher risk of developing diabetes than those who have more fat deposits on their hips or thighs (pear shaped obesity). Most doctors take into account *waist-to-hip ratio (WHR)* in determining how prone a person is to being a diabetic. Dividing the waist measurements by the hip measurements in inches determines this ratio. Men who have a *WHR* greater than 0.9 and women who have a *WHR* greater than 0.85 are more prone to diabetes. For example, if a person's waist measures 44 inches in circumference and the hips measure 40 inches in circumference the waist-to-hip ratio (WHR) is 1.1

Irregular and unhealthy food habits fluctuate the blood sugar levels erratically. Irregular eating habits (i.e. without any definite timing) or an increased intake of fats and refined and processed carbohydrates (bakery products, mithais, refined noodles, pastas etc.) can make a person prone to becoming a diabetic.

Stress has become an integral part of urban living. To cope with stress, some people overeat or reach for the wrong kind of foods while others may take to *alcohol or smoking* which can create the perfect setting that can lead to diabetes.

Diagnosis of Diabetes

The most common symptoms of diabetes that are easily detectable in the early stages are **increased urination (polyuria), increased thirst (polydypsia) and increased hunger (polyphagia).** Some individuals may also lose weight and strength as glucose utilization in the body is impaired. This situation is often referred to as '*poverty in the midst of plenty*'. This is because although there is plenty of sugar available in the blood, a diabetic person cannot utilize it, due to the disturbed or faulty utilization of sugar resulting from a lack of insulin.

The simplest and most reliable way to diagnose diabetes is to test **blood sugar levels** and **urine** for the presence of sugar.

The diagnostic criteria for Diabetes Mellitus is shown in the following table.

Categories	Fasting Blood Sugar Levels (mg/dl)	Post Lunch Blood Sugar Levels (mg/dl)
Normal	80 to 110	Less than 140
Impaired Glucose Tolerance	111 to 126	126 to 199
Diabetes	More than 126	More than 200

* WHO / ADA Criteria, 1999 (Venous Plasma Glucose).

<u>To explain the table above:</u>

▶ *Fasting blood sugar is a test done to check the sugar levels in the morning on an empty stomach.*
▶ *Post lunch blood sugar is the test done to check the sugar levels 2 hours after a meal. This is done to check how effectively the insulin functions to regulate blood sugar.*

A person is considered to be normal when his fasting blood sugar level is between 80 to 110 mg/dl and post lunch blood sugar levels is less than 140 mg/dl.

A fasting blood sugar level of 111 to 126 mg/dl and/or a post lunch blood sugar level of 126 to 199 mg/dl is said to be higher than the normal levels. This rise in blood sugar levels could be due to some other disease or ailment and not necessarily diabetes. The sugar levels probably rise because of impaired glucose tolerance which is not really diagnosed as diabetes. However, there is certainly a higher risk of developing diabetes. Consult a diabetologist about appropriate changes in your life style, diet and exercise which can help in preventing the progression of impaired glucose tolerance to diabetes.

A person is diagnosed as diabetic when either the fasting blood sugar levels are more than 126 mg/dl or post lunch blood sugar levels are more than 200 mg/dl. You need to be cautious and consult your diabetologist for tips to control blood sugar levels and prevent further complications.

Another screening test is to check the **presence of sugar in the urine**. In normal circumstances, sugar is never present in urine. Only when the blood sugar goes beyond a certain level, the extra sugar is spilled and is excreted through urine.

Types of Diabetes

Diabetes can be classified as:

▶ Type I Diabetes Mellitus (IDDM)
▶ Type II Diabetes Mellitus (NIDDM)
▶ Others

1. Type I Diabetes Mellitus accounts for all diabetics who are insulin dependent and therefore this type is also referred to as **Insulin Dependent Diabetes Mellitus** (IDDM). This category includes **juvenile diabetes** which is diabetes that occurs at a very young age. Those with type I diabetes mellitus are deficient in insulin and hence require external insulin injections to regulate their blood sugar levels life long.

2. Type II Diabetes Mellitus accounts for a large percentage of diabetics and is most common among individuals above the age of 35 to 40 years. Individuals with type II diabetes mellitus have a diminished secretion of insulin and hence they require oral drugs that will stimulate the pancreas to produce and secrete insulin. They do not have to take external insulin as part of their treatment and so this type of diabetes is referred as **Non Insulin Dependent Diabetes Mellitus** (NIDDM) or **adult onset diabetes.** It can be managed or its onset may be delayed by taking the necessary precautionary measures like looking after one's diet and monitoring weight by regular exercise while cutting down on sugary and fatty foods. However in some cases, when the insulin production decreases, there may be a need for external insulin, under a physicians guidance.

3. Other kinds of diabetes are **Gestational Diabetes Mellitus,** that occurs to mothers during their pregnancy and **Secondary Diabetes Mellitus** which is a broad category that includes diabetes caused due to certain genetic disorders, medical diseases, drugs and malignancies.

Hypoglycemia
(Low Blood Sugar Levels)

Hypoglycemia is by far the most common condition that diabetics face at some time or the other.

Diabetics who take insulin or oral hypoglycemic drugs are prone to low blood sugar levels after they have their medication. They must eat within a stipulated time period or their blood sugar may drop drastically leading to a condition called HYPOGLYCEMIA.

Another question that arises is, "How can one detect hypoglycemia ?" The most common signs and symptoms of a hypoglycemic are as listed below.

- ▸ Severe headaches early in the morning.
- ▸ Increased sweating and palpitations.
- ▸ Weakness and dizziness.
- ▸ Blurred vision and hunger pangs.
- ▸ Mood swings with or without slurred speech.
- ▸ Experiencing drowsiness.
- ▸ Nervousness with a confused state of mind.
- ▸ Bed wetting during the night.

These symptoms of hypoglycemia may vary for different individuals and also the same individuals may experience different symptoms at different times. Thus, one has to be alert at all times.

If you experience any of the above symptoms, consult your doctor immediately as self diagnosis or improper treatment for hypoglycemia can lead to unconsciousness or even convulsions in extreme situations. To combat hypoglycemia quickly and effectively to avoid any complications, have 2 biscuits or a small piece of milk chocolate or 2 teaspoons of glucon D dissolved in a glass of water or any other sweetened beverage.

Why does hypoglycemia occur?

- ▸ Overdose of medication i.e. if one has had too many pills or excess insulin. Also it's important to eat almost immediately after the medication.
- ▸ Delay in regular meal times or skipping one or more meals or a snack.
- ▸ Overexertion. In other words, if you exercise more than normal and are stressed out or overworked. Any kind of exertion that one is not accustomed to on a daily basis can affect the blood sugar levels.
- ▸ Consumption of alcohol on an empty stomach or when one already has low blood sugar levels.

Some individuals experience *hypoglycemia unawareness* which means that they undergo a stage of hypoglycemia but are not aware of it. Regular self-monitoring of blood sugar levels by using a glucometer is recommended for such diabetics under the supervision of a physician or diabetologist.

Hyperglycemia
(High Blood Sugar Levels)

This is a condition when the blood sugar levels are much higher than normal. Such **uncontrolled diabetes** can be fatal if it is not managed correctly or treated on time. It occurs only when the prescribed medication has not been taken or when the person is ill or undergoing severe stress.

The unutilized blood sugar has the following effects on our body.

▸ Increased urination and/or increased thirst.
▸ Dry mouth and dehydration.
▸ Pain in the calves.
▸ Loss of appetite.
▸ Weakness.
▸ Weight loss.
▸ Easy fatigability.
▸ Difficulty in breathing.
▸ High blood sugar levels may also lead to the presence of ketones in the urine. In extreme cases, your physician or diabetologist will recommend periodic blood and urine tests to check on the sugar and ketone levels. A fruity odour in the breath is a very common sign of high ketone levels in the urine.

Why does hyperglycemia occur?

▸ Undiagnosed diabetes.
▸ Change in medication like omission or reduction of external insulin or oral medicines.
▸ Infections or acute illness such as flu, cold, diarrhoea etc.
▸ Improper eating habits or incorrect selection of foods.

Consequences of Diabetes

"Prevention is better than Cure". The main aim of taking all the necessary precautions is to keep blood sugar levels in check and to minimize the risk of many complications associated with diabetes. These complications include **hypoglycemia** (low blood sugar levels), **kidney disease, neurological complications** (like damage to nerves, numbness of feet and hands and lack of sensation, loss of strength resulting in pain and weakness, slow healing of wounds and cuts and after an injury) **hypertension** and **heart disease** due to clogging of arteries and in **extreme cases diabetic ketoacidosis.**

All of these can be avoided or kept in control with proper dietary care and effective use of medication under your doctor's supervision. Let's see how we can look after diabetes......

Looking after Diabetes

Effective management of diabetes depends on a delicate balance between medication and diet control. The main goals in looking after diabetes are:

▶ **To achieve or to maintain ideal body weight.** Being overweight or underweight is equally harmful for a diabetic. Hence if one falls in either of the categories, do ensure that you take the necessary precautions to stay at your ideal body weight. You may now wonder what ideal body weight is and how we can determine our ideal body weight.

Here is a formula of Broca's Index to help you determine what weight is appropriate for your height.

For men : Height (cm) – 100 = Ideal body weight (kgs).
"100" mentioned in the formula is the standard figure for men to determine their ideal body weight according to their height.

For women: Height (cm)−105 = Ideal body weight (kgs).
"105" mentioned in the formula is the standard figure for women to determine their ideal body weight according to their height.

▸ **To maintain blood sugar levels** close to the normal levels. Refer to the table on page 13 for more information on blood sugar levels.

▸ **To improve overall physical and mental health** by following a balanced routine for exercise, diet and also minimizing stress levels as that also can aggravate the situation.

▸ **To maintain the blood cholesterol and triglyceride levels** as most diabetic patients are prone to heart disease. Avoid eating sugary and fried foods and also include plenty of fibre in your diet to cut down on any accumulated bad cholesterol.

▸ **To prevent or to delay any further health ailments associated with diabetes** by early detection and prompt treatment.

∼ ❧ Know your Nutrients ❧ ∼

A diabetic diet should consist of a good combination of nutrients i.e. carbohydrates, protein,,fat, vitamins and minerals to stay fit and fine and to keep the blood sugar levels in check.

Every adult requires approximately **2000 kilocalories** (or calories as we regularly say) every day to maintain optimum health. However, if a person is either obese or underweight then he needs to cut down or add on to these calories as recommended by a diabetologist or nutritionist.

Listed below are the nutrients you need to know about, along with their distribution you need in your daily diet.

1. Carbohydrates

Carbohydrates should fulfil approximately 60 to 65% of our daily energy (caloric) intake .

A common misconception is that most carbohydrates are regarded as sugars, as a result of which they are completely avoided in the diabetic diet, whereas in actual fact what is necessary is that one should choose carbohydrates carefully.

Carbohydrates are divided into two groups, viz. simple carbohydrates and complex carbohydrates. **Simple carbohydrates** like sugar, honey, jaggery etc. do not need to be metabolized and hence will raise the blood sugar levels immediately. These should be avoided. Refined cereals like maida, pasta, semolina etc. should also be restricted as the process of refining breaks down these complex carbohydrates into simple carbohydrates that raise the blood sugar levels rapidly.

On the other hand, consumption of **complex carbohydrates** such as whole wheat, jowar, bajra, oats, brown rice (instead of white rice) etc. should be given more emphasis. These complex carbohydrates are preferred as they take longer to digest and thus give rise to a gradual increase in blood sugar levels, making it easier for a diabetic person to adjust to the changes in blood sugar levels.

The important thing for diabetics is not to completely restrict their consumption of carbohydrates, but to alter the type of carbohydrates consumed. For example, it is better to have unpolished or brown rice instead of polished white rice.

A simple way to find out how quickly foods raise your blood sugar levels is by means of the **glycemic index. Foods with a high glycemic index are those that raise the blood sugar levels very rapidly.**
It is a misconception that only table sugar shoots up the blood sugar levels rapidly. The glycemic index shows that certain foods like potato, yam etc. also show a

rapid increase in blood sugar levels and are hence termed as high glycemic index foods.

It is advisable for diabetics to consume foods with a low glycemic index (as they bring about a gradual rise in the blood sugar levels) such as guava, plums, cluster beans, broccoli, cauliflower etc. and to mix foods with medium glycemic index such as pineapple, muskmelon, pastas etc. with low glycemic index foods.

2. Protein

This nutrient is required for the regular maintenance of our body and repairs the wear and tear of body tissues. **Protein should form approximately 12 to 20% of our daily caloric (energy) intake.**

It is essential to include protein in our diet, but only just enough to meet our daily requirements as excess protein puts a lot of burden on the kidneys to excrete its by-products.

We need not drastically reduce the protein in our diet, but should consume it in moderation. Try and include only one source of protein in each meal. For example, either eggs or milk for breakfast, either curds or dal for lunch or dinner etc. Avoid having dal, paneer and curds in the same meal as that becomes a very heavy dose of protein.

3. Fat

Fat is a concentrated source of energy and it makes us feel satiated. It is also necessary for our body in small quantities as apart from calories (1 gm. of oil or fat = 9 calories), it contains essential fatty acids which are required to perform certain vital functions in our body. Since these fatty acids cannot be produced naturally by our body, if we do not consume the recommended amount of fat per day, our body becomes deficient in these fatty acids causing visible symptoms like fatigue, weakness, mood swings, dry skin and dry hair.

Oil also helps in the absorption of fat-soluble vitamins like **A, D, E and K.** Vitamins A and E are important in our daily diet, as they are antioxidants which means they help us to build up our immune system to fight against infections. Vitamin D helps in strengthening our bones and teeth, whereas vitamin K helps in clotting the blood in case of injuries.

Care should be taken in choosing the right type of fat, to prevent another common consequence of diabetes viz.. heart disease. Oil, butter, vanaspati or ghee which of these is better? We often wonder.... Well, here are the answers to that.

Oil is a healthier cooking option, although you can include small amounts of ghee and butter, using them sparingly. It is advisable for healthy individuals to consume no more than 6 teaspoons of fat (30 grams) per day and for diabetics not more than **3 teaspoons of fat per day** to avoid any health complications. Another way of keeping count is to measure out ½ litre (approx. ½ kg) per person per month. This recommendation is for diabetics with normal blood cholesterol and triglyceride levels. In case your levels are higher, check with your diabetologist or nutritionist as to whether to cut down on fat or change the type of fat you are using.

Excessive fat apart from making us put on weight can also disturb the absorption of important nutrients like calcium in our body.

4. Fibre

Fibre is a complex carbohydrate present in foods and although it is not really a 'nutrient', it is nevertheless an important component of our diet. It cleans up our system, prevents constipation and reduces blood cholesterol and triglyceride levels thus helping to prevent heart disease.
Our diet should include approximately 15 to 25 grams of fibre daily.

Fibre is extremely essential for diabetics, as it satiates us for longer periods and due to its low glycemic index causes slow release of sugar in the blood stream, thus helping to control diabetes. This also improves the efficiency of insulin in the cells and hence may decrease the need for external insulin if the person is insulin dependent. Fibre is found only in foods derived from plants and how much depends on whether it has been processed. For example, unpolished rice contains much more fibre than processed or polished rice.

Here are some easy ways to include fibre in your diet.

▸ Start the day with a high fibre dish like Green Pea Pancakes, page 80.
▸ Have plenty of vegetables, especially raw vegetables in the form of salads and raitas. Do not peel vegetables and fruits like cucumber, carrot, apples etc. as their peels are edible and much of the fibre is present just beneath their peels. However if you want to scrape the peel, do so very lightly and remember to wash them thoroughly before eating to make them completely free of germs and pesticides.
▸ Eat high fibre foods like dried peas, beans and lentils.
▸ Choose brown bread or rotis made with whole wheat flour instead of instead of bread, pasta or rotis made from refined flour (maida).
▸ Try to use the bran of cereals like wheat, oats and rice in your regular meals. For example, adding 1 tablespoon of bran in the chapati dough or in the vegetable dishes will provide plenty of fibre. Bran is also a good thickening agent that can add low calorie bulk to soups, gravies etc. Bran is easily available at most health food stores and larger grocery stores.

5. Vitamins and Minerals

Vitamins and minerals are needed for the regular maintenance of our body. Iron (for blood formation), calcium (bones and teeth), folic acid (for maintenance of body cells), vitamin A (for clear vision and glowing skin), vitamin D (for the absorption of calcium in our body), vitamin E (for healthy skin), vitamin K (helps in clotting blood during injuries), B group vitamin (for metabolism of carbohydrates, protein and fat) and vitamin C (helps in building immunity).

Fresh leafy vegetables like spinach (palak), cow pea (chawli) leaves etc. and other vegetables like cabbage, cauliflower etc. are an excellent source of these vitamins and minerals. Fresh fruits like orange, sweet lime, apple etc. also contribute substantially by providing vitamins and minerals to our diet.

Along with the above nutrients, one very important part of our diet is **fluids**. They are required to flush all the wastes out and to maintain the fluid (water) balance in our body.

Diabetics need to have plenty of fluids as they help to keep the urine diluted, so that the kidneys can flush it out without being taxed.

Water is not the only source of fluid that one can have. Vegetable soups and broths are beneficial too. Avoid carbonated beverages as far as possible as these provide no real nutrients, but only empty calories, which means they only help in weight gain. For example, one 12-oz bottle of carbonated beverage has approximately 9 teaspoons of sugar. Restrict the consumption of tea and coffee to 2 cups per day as caffeine hinders with the absorption of important nutrients like iron in our body. Try and avoid the consumption of fruit juices too as they contain plenty of sugar and because plenty of fruit is required to make 1 glass of juice. To add to this, juices also does not add any fibre as most of it is strained which in turn can raise the blood sugar levels instantaneously.

Diet and Diabetes

Diabetes is a condition that requires us to take special care of our diet. The quality and the quantity of the food we eat needs to be monitored carefully as minor changes in our meal habits can lead to either low blood sugar levels (hypoglycemia) or high blood sugar levels (hyperglycemia). Refer to pages 15 and 17 for more information on low and high blood sugar levels.

A good meal plan should fit with your schedule and eating habits. The right meal plan will also help to maintain your ideal body weight.

The best way to deal with diabetes is with a balanced combination of medication and a carefully planned diet. One should always try to follow the meal plans prescribed by a diabetologist or nutritionist. Also maintain regular meal timings to avoid drastic fluctuations in the blood sugar levels. Do not delay meals or snacks especially after medication.

Some diabetics cannot manage to consume large meals at a time and need to distribute their food intake by having frequent small meals throughout the day. This regulates the blood sugar levels and avoids hypoglycemia (low blood sugar). For sample diabetic menus refer to page 159 and 160.

Here are some simple and handy ways to maintain blood sugar levels.

▸ Have a balanced diet which includes complex cereals, pulses, fruits and vegetables. In cereals, whole wheat is better than rice because it contains **an enzyme called Ascarbose, which allows carbohydrate to be absorbed slowly.** Thus, the blood sugar does not rise rapidly.

▸ Have only **one source of protein** like dal, low fat milk or curds in each meal. If you are used to having thick dal, try to dilute it, as that will cut down on the protein content drastically. Even the buttermilk you consume should be diluted with water to reduce the intake of concentrated protein.

- Consume **plenty of fibre-rich foods** such as whole cereals, pulses, raw vegetables and fruits. These help to lower blood sugar levels, as they have a low glycemic index and lead to a gradual increase in the blood sugar levels. On the other hand, restrict all fruit juices and fruits like mango, chickoo, custard apple, banana as they have a high sugar content. Also restrict starchy vegetables like potatoes, yam etc. as these tend to increase the blood sugar levels rapidly.
- **Restrict the consumption of fat to 3 teaspoons per day**. Avoid snacking on fried foods like samosas, wafers etc. as these are unhealthy. Have cereals, fruits, vegetables and grilled, boiled or stir-fried dishes.
- Try and **avoid processed and refined foods** such as maida, noodles etc. as they have a high glycemic index and can escalate the blood sugar levels very rapidly. These foods have virtually no fibre and so are not very healthy. The biggest culprits are bakery products and savoury farsans.
- **Avoid sugar, jaggery and honey**. Also, avoid the consumption of sweets such as barfi, halwa, jams, jellies etc. Use artificial sweeteners instead, but again remember, moderation is the key. Consult your diabetologist or nutritionist for the choice and the quantity of artificial sweeteners to be consumed.
- **Avoid all nuts and dry fruits** as they are high in saturated fats. As said earlier saturated fats get converted to cholesterol in our body and tend to increase our blood cholesterol levels.
- Try and **avoid the consumption of carbonated beverages** as these provide no real nutrients but only empty calories which means calories that can increase your weight.
- **Use artifical sweetners in moderation.** Consult your doctor for the choice and amount of sweetners to be consumed.
- If there is any **change in your schedule, either in meal timings or of other activities, please consult your diabetologist or nutritionist to adjust your medication to suit your new schedule.**
- Have an early dinner before retiring for the night and have a glass of low fat milk at least 1½ and 2 hours after dinner as this helps to prevent hypoglycemia (low blood sugar levels) during the night. For more information on hypoglycemia, refer to page 15.

- ▸ Try to **eat in a calm atmosphere** as stress or anxiety can impair the production of insulin.
- ▸ **Read the nutritional labels on food packages** carefully for proper selection of foods, particularly those claiming to be low fat foods. Low fat products may actually contain more fat than you think.
- ▸ **Walk for 15 to 20 minutes after every meal** as exercise utilizes the sugar present in blood and helps insulin work better. In case you do indulge in a favourite dessert compensate for it by walking a little more.

Cooking Healthy

A healthy balanced diet isn't just about eating the right kind of food. **The way that we buy, store, prepare and cook our food and even the pots, pans and equipment we use, all have a significant impact on the nutritive value of our meals.** The aim should be to cook tasty food, to limit the consumption of oil-laden foods and to incorporate plenty of vegetables, fruits, cereals and pulses in our regular diet.

To limit the use of fat in your daily diet, here are some handy tips.

▶ Use **non-stick cookware** as they require less oil to cook food.

▶ **Bake, steam or sauté,** instead of shallow frying and deep-frying.

▶ Use a **pressure cooker** to cook vegetables, as pressure cooking requires less oil. This method also helps one to conserve the nutrients that are volatile, as the closed lid prevents the loss of nutrients.

▶ **Avoid the use of nuts like coconut, cashewnuts etc.** Replace the gravies made with cashewnuts or khus–khus paste with a vegetable purée like cauliflower or pumpkin purée. Use tomato gravy as in the recipe of Stuffed Karelas in Makhani Gravy, page 63, or use pumpkin to thicken a vegetable dish, as in the recipe of Gavar Pumpkin Vegetable, page 62.

▶ **Choose skim milk and its products in place of whole milk.** Skim milk provides all the goodness of milk without the fat. Try and use paneer (cottage cheese) made at home using skim milk instead of buying it from the market. Preparing skim milk at home does not demand much effort from your side. Believe me, it is very easy to prepare. All you need to do is boil the milk and skim the fat layer (malai) that is formed after it has been cooled. Repeat this procedure at least twice or thrice to get almost fat free milk. An easier way to make skim milk is to mix skim milk powder with water. Use this low fat milk to make curds and paneer. I have included easy recipes for Low Fat Curds, page 153, and Low Fat Paneer, page 154.

▶ **Avoid salads with oil-based dressings like mayonnaise.** Make innovative low fat dressings made with low fat curds as in the recipe of

Lemony Yoghurt Salad, page 121, or an oil free soya sauce and lemon dressing as in the recipe of Cucumber Salad, page 114.

▸ **Be aware of hidden fats present in foods** like peanuts, sesame seeds, walnuts or cashewnuts, cakes, sweet savouries, cream biscuits, chocolates and popcorn made with butter or oil. Very often, we binge on these calorie-laden foods believing them to be not so fatty as fat is not as visible like in deep-fried foods.

∽ Food Exchange List ∽

I often wondered whether it is possible for a diabetic to follow a rigid meal plan throughout their life without indulging once in a while or succumbing to an occasional Chocolate Brownie....
Fortunately, that's possible and the food exchange list will help you to do just that.

As this system allows you to exchange one food with the other on the same list, it is referred as FOOD EXCHANGE LIST.

Every food on a particular list has approximately the same calories, carbohydrates, protein and fat content. One serving (exchange) of each of these foods are equal and can be exchanged for any other food on the same list.

This list provides us with a large variety of food choices that we can substitute our favourite foods with while also controlling the balance of calories, carbohydrates, protein and fat throughout the day so that the blood sugar level does not fluctuate erratically.
For example, to be able to enjoy a pastry, you can exchange it with approx. ½ exchange of cereal, ½ exchange of low fat milk and 1 exchange of fat.

According to this list, all major food groups are divided into 7 separate categories. Each group consists of a list of foods/ ingredients along with their recommended serving sizes that a diabetic person can indulge in with relative safety.

The food exchange list has been divided into 7 major groups as follows:

1. Cereal/Starch
2. Pulses
3. Vegetables
4. Fruits
5. Milk and Dairy Products
6. Fat
7. Meat

Listed below are many of the ingredients commonly included in the Indian diet along with their recommended serving sizes that can be exchanged with another food in the same group as they have approximately the same nutritive values. If there is any particular food that is not included on this food exchange list, ask your nutritionist for more information.

1. Cereal/Starch

Each item in this list contains approximately 100 calories, 23.5 grams of carbohydrates, 3 grams of protein and a trace of fat. All the ingredients have been listed alphabetically and each ingredient can be substituted with another ingredient in this list.

Ingredient	Exchange
Bajra (black millet), raw	3 tablespoons
Bajra flour (black millet flour)	¼ cup
Barley (jau), raw	2½ tablespoons
Broken wheat (dalia), raw	2½ tablespoons
Buckwheat (kutto or kutti no daro), raw	2½ tablespoons
Jowar (white millet), raw	2½ tablespoons
Jowar flour (white millet flour)	⅓ cup
Makai ka atta (maize flour)	¾ cup
Poha (flaked rice)	½ cup
Puffed rice (mumara)	2 cups
Quick rolled oats, raw	⅓ cup
Ragi (nachni) flour	¼ cup
Refined flour (maida)	¼ cup

Continued...

Ingredient	Exchange
Rice flour (chawal ka atta)	¼ cup
Rice, cooked	⅔ cup
Rice, parboiled, raw	2 tablespoons
Semolina (rawa), raw	2½ tablespoons
Varagu (kodri), raw	½ cup
Wheat flour (gehun ka atta)	¼ cup
Whole wheat bread	2 slices
Whole wheat pasta, cooked	1 cup

2. Pulses

Each item in this list contains approximately 100 calories, 17 grams of carbohydrates, 7 grams of protein and a trace of fat. All the ingredients have been listed alphabetically and each ingredient can be substituted with another ingredient in this list.

Ingredient	Exchange
Bengal gram flour (besan)	⅓ cup
Black eyed beans (lobhia), cooked	⅓ cup
Chana dal (split Bengal gram), cooked	⅓ cup
Chick peas (kabuli chana), cooked	⅓ cup
Masoor (whole red lentil), cooked	⅓ cup
Masoor dal (split red lentil), cooked	⅓ cup
Matki (moath beans), cooked	½ cup
Moong (whole green gram), cooked	¾ cup
Moong dal (split green gram), cooked	⅓ cup
Moong dal flour (green gram flour)	2 tablespoons
Rajma (kidney beans), cooked	⅔ cup
Red chana (whole red gram), cooked	2 tablespoons
Soya chunks, cooked	⅔ cup
Soya flour	⅓ cup
Soya granules, cooked	½ cup
Soyabean, cooked	⅓ cup
Toovar (arhar) dal, cooked	⅓ cup
Urad dal (split black gram), cooked	⅓ cup
Vaal (field beans), cooked	⅔ cup

3. Vegetables

Each item in this list contains approximately 25 calories, 5 grams of carbohydrates, 1 gram of protein and a trace of fat. All the ingredients have been listed alphabetically and each ingredient can be substituted with another ingredient in this list.

Ingredient	Exchange
Asparagus, chopped	½ cup
Baby corn	4 nos.
Beetroot, chopped	¾ cup
Bhindi (ladies finger), chopped	1 cup
Bottle gourd (lauki/doodhi), chopped	2 cups
Brinjal (baingan/eggplant), chopped	1 cup
Broccoli, grated	1 cup
Cabbage, chopped	1 cup
Capsicum, chopped	1 cup
Carrot, chopped	⅓ cup
Cauliflower, grated	1 cup
Celery stalks, chopped	1¼ cups
Cluster beans (gavarfali), chopped	1½ cups
Chawli (cow pea) leaves, chopped	1 cup
Coriander leaves, chopped	2 cups
Cucumber, chopped	1⅓ cups
Dill (shepu), chopped	3 cups
Drumstick, chopped	1¼ cups
Fenugreek (methi) leaves, chopped	2 cups
French beans, chopped	1 cup
Green peas	¼ cup
Kand (purple yam), chopped *	¼ cup
Karela (bitter gourd), sliced	1 cup
Lettuce, chopped	¾ cup
Mushrooms, chopped	1¼ cups
Onion, chopped	⅓ cup
Papdi beans, chopped	⅔ cup
Potato, chopped *	¼ cup
Radish (mooli) leaves, chopped	2 cups

Continued...

It put the sweetness back in my diet.
And the smile back on my face.

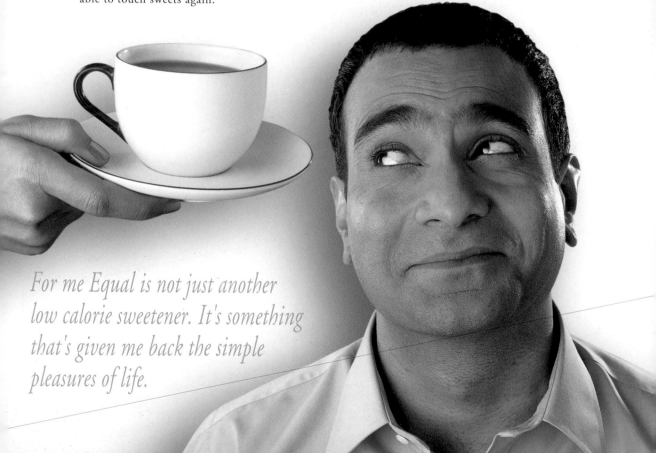

If I had to list down the three happiest days of my life, this is what they would be: first, the day my girlfriend (and now my wife) agreed to marry me; second, the day our daughter was born; and third, the day I discovered Equal.

Puzzled at the last one? You see, for me Equal is not just another low calorie sweetener. It's something that has given me back the simple pleasures of life. And made me immeasurably happy.

Let me begin from the beginning. Five years ago when the doctor told me I had diabetes, I was crushed. I, who had an incurable sweet tooth, who couldn't keep his hands off a steaming bowl of halwa, for whom a meal was incomplete without topping it up with a sweet dish, I had to stay away from sweets for the rest of my life. It was unthinkable. Feelings of denial, anger, hopelessness and insecurity overwhelmed me. My family rallied around me, tried to cheer me up. Their love and support helped me overcome my misery. But a void remained. That of never being able to touch sweets again.

For me Equal is not just another low calorie sweetener. It's something that's given me back the simple pleasures of life.

Five years ago when the doctor told me I had diabetes, I was crushed. Feelings of denial, anger, hopelessness and insecurity overwhelmed me.

Wherever I went, be it a family dinner or an office gathering, sweets tempted me. They seemed more alluring than ever before. It was hard to turn away. Believe me, it was hard.

And then one day the dark clouds parted. It was the day a friend, a fellow-diabetic, told me about Equal. It's a low calorie sweetener, he said, a safe substitute for sugar for people like you and me, since it's made of aspartame*. Diabetics and health-conscious people across the world are using it. In fact, Equal is the world's leading brand of low calorie sweeteners, he added. It's available in powder and tablet form, the former for preparing sweet dishes and the latter in drinks like tea and nimbu paani. Both forms have negligible calories, he informed me. If you do a comparison, while one spoon of sugar contains 20 calories, one spoon of Equal Spoonful (powder form) contains only 2 and an Equal tablet contains barely 0.33. And best of all, one tablet of Equal (or for that matter, one teaspoon of Equal Spoonful) is equal to one spoon of sugar in sweetness. In other words, Equal tastes as sweet as sugar. It sounded too good to be true.

Naturally, I wasted no time in bringing Equal home. And finally, after two long, agonising years, I got to do the things I'd craved for. Drinking sweetened tea. Sinking my teeth into a shahi tukda. Treating myself to a bowl of kheer. I was happy. Truly, deeply happy.

Sweets seemed more alluring than ever before. It was hard to turn away.

*A dietary component found naturally.

Equal is the world's leading brand of low calorie sweetener. And best of all, it tastes as good as sugar.

Today I see this happiness reflected in the faces of my wife and daughter. They needn't feel guilty anymore having sweets in front of me. I am no longer the odd one out at the dining table. Life seems complete. Equal has filled the void.

I don't look at diabetes as an ailment now. It's just a condition I have to keep under control. And I'm doing a pretty good job of that. More so because of the positive frame of mind I have developed. I feel fitter, healthier, happier than I have in a long, long time.

Thank you, Equal.

For more information and a free Equal Spoonful Recipe Booklet, write to lowcal@merisant.com or to P.O. Box 9605, New Delhi - 58.

Not recommended for children*. Not for Phenylketoneurics.

*Since children are in the growth phase, they need extra calories. However, Equal doesn't have any adverse effect on children.

I am no longer the odd one out at the dining table. I feel fitter, healthier, happier than I have in a long, long time.

EQUaL
LOW CALORIE SWEETENER
Spoonful

TASTE OF SUGAR ...
IS THE CALORIES

EQUaL
LOW CALORIE SWEETENER

TASTES LIKE SUGAR

...ng suggestions only

Bring back the sweetness.

Ingredient	Exchange
Radish (mooli), sliced	1 cup
Red pumpkin (kaddu), chopped	1 cup
Spinach (palak), chopped	1cup
Spring onions, chopped	1 cup
Suran (yam), chopped *	¼ cup
Sweet corn, whole (raw)	¾ cup
Sweet potato, chopped *	2 tablespoons
Tendli, chopped	1 cup
Tomato, chopped	¾ cup
Turai (ridge gourd), chopped	2 cups

* Foods to be consumed in restricted amounts.

4. Fruits

Each item in this list contains approximately 40 calories, 10 grams of carbohydrates, 1 gram of protein and a trace of fat. All the ingredients have been listed alphabetically and each ingredient can be substituted with another ingredient in this list.

Ingredient	Exchange
Apple, chopped	½ cup
Banana, chopped *	⅛ cup
Black jamun	7 nos.
Cherry, chopped	⅓ cup
Chickoo, chopped *	⅓ cup
Custard apple *	¼ cup
Grapes, medium *	⅓ cup
Guava, chopped	½ cup
Mango, chopped *	⅓ cup
Muskmelon (kharbooja), chopped	1½ cups
Orange, segmented	½ cup
Papaya, chopped	1 cup
Peach, chopped	⅔ cup
Pears, chopped	⅔ cup
Pineapple, chopped	½ cup

Continued...

Ingredient	Exchange
Plum, sliced	½ cup
Pomegranate (anar)	½ cup
Strawberries, quartered	¾ cup
Sweet lime, segmented	½ cup
Watermelon (tarbuj), chopped	1½ cups
White jamun	3 nos.

Foods to be consumed in restricted amounts.

5. Milk

Each item in this list contains approximately 80 calories, 12 grams of carbohydrates, 8 gram of protein and a trace of fat. All the ingredients have been listed alphabetically and each ingredient can be substituted with another ingredient in this list.

Ingredient	Exchange
Cheese, shredded *	¼ cup
Low fat milk	1 cup
Low fat curds	1 cup
Low fat paneer, chopped	¼ cup

Foods to be consumed in restricted amounts.

6. Fat

Each item in this list contains approximately 45 calories, no carbohydrates, no protein and 5 grams of fat. All the ingredients have been listed alphabetically and each ingredient can be substituted with another ingredient in this list.

Ingredient	Exchange
Butter *	1 teaspoon
Oil / Ghee *	1 teaspoon

Foods to be consumed in restricted amounts.

Lean meat (white meat) contains approximately 55 calories, no carbohydrates, 7 grams of protein and 3 grams of fat whereas high fat meat (red meat) contains approximately 100 calories, no carbohydrates, 7 grams of protein and 8 grams of fat.

As this is a vegetarian cookbook, I have not mentioned the nutritive values of individual meats. Please consult your nutritionist for more information.

A Brief Look at Foods Allowed, Restricted and Forbidden

All these foods should be eaten according to the serving sizes that are mentioned on the Food Exchange List, pages 30 to 34.

Foods Allowed

These are foods with a low glycemic index and hence a large part of the diet should comprise of these foods. Foods with a low glycemic index increase the blood sugar gradually and so are good for diabetics.

▶ Complex cereals like whole wheat, whole wheat noodles, bajra, jowar, ragi (nachni), wheat bran, rice bran, barley etc.
▶ Dals and pulses like moong dal, tur dal, rajma, moong etc.
▶ All vegetables like cabbage, brinjal, cluster beans, spinach, fenugreek etc. except those mentioned in the restricted list like potatoes, yam and sweet potatoes.
▶ Low fat dairy products like milk, curds, paneer and buttermilk.
▶ Fruits with low sugar and high water content like watermelon, pineapple etc. Have only one serving of fruit at a time. Refer to the exchange list for serving size (page 33).

Restricted Foods

These are foods with a high glycemic index which can escalate blood sugar levels faster than foods with a low glycemic index. Indulge in these foods in moderation and only as an occasional treat.

- Sugar rich fruits like chickoo, custard apple, grapes and mango.
- Vegetables such as potatoes, yam, purple yam and sweet potato.
- Highly refined foods like maida, pasta made with refined flour etc.
- Polished rice.
- Biscuits such as Digestive and Marie.
- Artificial sweeteners.
- Restrict the intake of fat to 3 teaspoons per day.
- Cheese

Forbidden Foods

These foods are best avoided as they can cause harm to our health and have little or no nutritive value. These can escalate the blood sugar levels almost instantaneously.

- Refined sugar, honey, jaggery, jam and jellies.
- Deep fried foods like wafers, samosas, farsan etc.
- High fat salad dressings which use cream, mayonnaise etc.
- Fruit juices as they rapidly increase the blood sugar levels. Instead, it is better to have a whole fruit as it contains fibre which is beneficial to regulate the blood sugar levels.
- Aerated drinks, preserved or canned fruit and fruit squash which contain loads of sugar as preservative.
- Alcohol.
- Nuts like dried cashewnuts, almonds etc. as they are high in saturated fat.
- Sweetmeats like peda, barfi and all other mithai.
- Chocolates, puddings and pies, full fat ice-creams, biscuits made with refined flour, high sugar and cream content.

❦ Eating Out ❦

Rigorous diet restrictions are probably easy to live with if you're eating at home. But eating out either at a restaurant or with company can lead to uncomfortable situations, especially if you have to ask the hostess to prepare a special meal for you. Sometimes, we tend to cut down on our socializing to avoid the embarrassment.

If you know that you will be dining out, prepare for it in advance.

▶ If the dinner is going to be served late, have soup or a small snack along with your medication before you start out. The trick here is that if you leave for the party on an empty stomach, we are tempted to binge on whatever we can lay our hands on first. Whereas if we have snacked a little before the party, we can reason and choose our food wisely.

▶ It's easy to get tempted or flustered if we happen to see only spicy and oily food around you. Be wise and try to select the best of the lot. Eat small portions and have a snack when you get back home, if you are still hungry.

▶ In case cocktails are being served, have an unsweetened fresh lime with soda instead of an aerated drink or an alcoholic beverage.

▶ Choose appetizers wisely. Avoid the fried ones and munch on vegetable crud{'i'}tiés or a salad.

▶ If you are not sure of any of the dishes being served, do not hesitate to ask the hostess or your server (in case of restaurants) for the ingredients used in a particular dish.

▶ Choose chapatis or phulkas instead of naans as the latter are made of refined flour i.e. maida.

▶ Select a stir-fried or sautéed vegetable dish rather than vegetables with gravy (as gravies may contain fatty ingredients like coconut, cashewnuts and plenty of oil). If you're eating at a restaurant, ask the server to request the chef to use less oil in your dishes.

▶ Try and avoid plain rice as it has a tendency to increase the blood sugar levels very rapidly. Always select a rice dish with a good combination of vegetables as they are rich in fibre and hence help to control the blood sugar levels.

- Have plenty of salads, but choose the dressings carefully. Always select low fat salad dressings or salads with a hint of lemon juice and other flavouring agents like herbs, pepper, soya sauce etc.
- Choose clear soups over creamy ones as thick and creamy soups have oodles of butter and refined flour (maida) that is used to thicken it.
- Have plain dals instead of the 'tadka' dals which have an unhealthy amount of butter or ghee added to temper and flavour it.
- Order grilled, steamed or roasted dishes as compared to deep fried ones.
- Enjoy an occasional treat like a pastry or an ice-cream but remember to have it in moderation and also in accordance with the food exchange list. If you're having a dessert, try and share it with someone so that you're not obliged to finish the whole portion. Choose a fruit based dessert over a cream based one. If you indulge in a dessert, try and compensate for that treat with other foods in the same meal. For example, if you know you want to eat dessert, then skip either the appetizer or the rice dish.

Exercise and Diabetes

Physical activity for a diabetic person is very important. It should be an integral part of our lifestyle. One should try and maintain a moderate and regular exercise regime throughout one's life.

Exercise can help us to burn the excess fat in the body and can thus help us lose excessive weight. Regular exercise also helps to regulate the blood sugar levels and to improve the action of insulin. Exercise also improves the heart's efficiency to pump blood.

It is important for diabetics to remember to eat a carbohydrate rich snack like 2 low fat biscuits or a small khakhra before beginning the exercise routine to avoid hypoglycemia (low blood sugar levels).

To avoid complications, do consult a physician or diabetologist before starting any exercise to confirm your medical fitness. He will also help you to choose a form of exercise that is suitable for your activity levels, age and lifestyle.

Today, the urban lifestyle does not allow us to exercise during the day. We have become dependent on transportation and technology like elevators, escalators, taxis, cars, and buses. Even at work, most of us have sedentary lifestyles and we do not even walk a couple of minutes each day. All these factors coupled with stress and unhealthy eating habits aggravate the problem and encourage obesity which is the root cause for many urban diseases.

Exercising regularly also decreases our stress levels and makes us happier and healthier individuals. It is wisest to choose a form of exercise comfortable to your lifestyle. For example, swimming, brisk walking, aerobics and yoga. Alternatively, you can indulge in a game of your choice like tennis, badminton etc.

Brisk walking is the best form of exercise as it helps to reduce the cholesterol levels in the blood. Most doctors recommend a regular brisk walk for at least 20 to 30 minutes daily.

Exercise raises the High Density Lipoprotein (HDL) levels, which is also called good cholesterol and decreases the bad cholesterol also known as Low Density Lipoprotein (LDL) levels. High HDL (good cholesterol) levels help to remove the cholesterol deposits from our body, thus preventing heart disease.

One need not set aside a special time or routine for exercising if it is included in our daily activities like taking the stairs instead of using the elevator, walking short distances instead of taking a cab, taking a small walk after lunch or dinner or picking up the groceries instead of having them delivered, as this works out your arms too.

Alcohol and Diabetes

Alcohol is becoming an important part of our lifestyles and is sadly considered acceptable on most social occasions such as weddings, social gatherings and as part of our work culture too. Going for a beer after work seems to be becoming a normal thing to do.

Alcohol provides approximately 7 kcal per gram and unfortunately these are empty calories which get deposited as fat reserves in our body. This means that it only provides calories without any nutrients and thus leads to weight gain.

If you must have alcohol, here are a few pointers to keep in mind.

▶ Avoid cocktails as they are usually made with calorie laden sweet mixers like juices, cream and aerated beverages. Try a calorie free drink mixer like soda, tonic water or water. Refer to the table of Common Alcoholic Combinations, page 41, to discover the difference yourself.

▶ Since alcohol has a tendency to lower blood sugar levels (hypoglycemia), restricting its intake is very important for diabetics, as one can become hypoglycemic. If you wish to have an occasional drink, never do so on an empty stomach.

▶ Have a low fat and carbohydrate rich snack to keep you going. Alternatively, have your drink with a light meal or a snack, avoiding deep fried foods and calorie-laden munchies. Try Hummus, page 98, or Baked Tortilla Chips, page 92, with Tomato Salsa, page 94, instead.

▶ Drink only when and if the blood sugar levels are in control. Even if it is a special occasion, avoid alcohol when your blood sugar levels are not in control. Do not plan to drive for several hours after you have had a drink.

▶ If you drink more than occasionally, ask your nutritionist to work it in your diet plan so that it does the minimum harm to your body. Also he/she will recommend the kind of alcohol that you should have. For example, 1 alcoholic beverage equals to 12- oz of beer, 5-oz glass of wine or 1 ½ oz of distilled spirits like whiskey, gin etc. 1 serving of alcohol is equal to 2 fat servings on the food exchange list. Check out the caloric value of alcohol in the table below:

Caloric Value of Alcoholic Beverages

Alcoholic Beverage	Amount	Calories
Beer	12 oz (approx. 330 ml)	178
Wine	60 ml	63
Port Wine	60 ml	95
Gin	30 ml	73
Rum	30 ml	73
Whisky	30 ml	73
Vodka	30 ml	73
Brandy	30 ml	77

Common Alcoholic Combinations

Alcoholic Beverage	Amount	Calories
Wine + Soda (Spritzer)	30 ml + 100 ml	34
Gin + Lemonade	30 ml + 220 ml	169
Gin + Tonic water	30 ml + 220 ml	73
Rum + Coke	30 ml + 220 ml	169
Rum + Water	30 ml + 220 ml	73
Whisky + Coke	30 ml + 220 ml	169
Whisky + Soda	30 ml + 220 ml	79
Vodka + Orange Juice	30 ml + 220 ml	284
Vodka + Tonic water	30 ml + 220 ml	73

❦ Nature Cures ❦
Home Remedies for Diabetes

" Nature cure is the best " is what all of us believe. Yes, nature has blessed us with some dietary adjuncts to control diabetes too. Listed below are a few of them.

Source	Form	Frequency to consume	Effect
Bitter gourd (Karela)	½ cup juice with seeds or 1 cup of cooked vegetable.	Should be consumed daily on empty stomach or in between meals.	The high insulin dose of this plant helps to reduce blood and urine sugar levels.
Amla (Indian gooseberry)	A tablespoon of amla juice with a cup of karela juice is helpful.	Daily. Try at least for 2 months for effective results.	This mixture helps to reduce the blood sugar in diabetics because of its low glycemic index.
Fenugreek (methi)	Fenugreeek leaves and seeds. In case of seeds soak one teaspoon of seeds overnight.	Half a cup of leaves should be consumed daily. Alternatively one teaspoon of seeds twice a day with milk are also helpful.	This is considered to be an effective supportive therapy for the management of diabetes.
Spirulina	Leaves or dried powder or tablets (1 daily).	Half a cup of leaves should be consumed daily. As these leaves are not very easily available, half teaspoon of dried powder can be taken everyday.	The soluble fibre in it stabilizes the blood sugar and cholesterol levels.
Neem and Basil leaves	Leaves or dried powder.	A few neem and basil leaves everyday. In case you can't find fresh leaves, half teaspoon of dried powder can be taken everyday.	Lowers blood sugar levels.
Onion	Raw, in salads, raita, etc.	Daily, at least 1 cup.	Has diuretic and digestive property and also helps to maintain blood sugar levels.

Continued...

Source	Form	Frequency to consume	Effect
Garlic	Fresh (crushed)	Daily, at least 1 large clove.	Helps to control blood sugar levels.
Black Jamun	Fruit or seed powder. An equal quantity of jamun powder, amla powder and karela powder is useful.	Consume 3 to 4 pieces of jamun fruit or a teaspoonful of the dried mixture once or twice a day.	Contains jamboline which helps to control the blood sugar levels.
Soyabean	Whole beans, sprouts, soya milk or soya flour.	Half cup of beans or a quarter cup of sprouts or half cup of milk or half cup of flour.	Rich in choline which is effective in controlling diabetes and also helps in preventing neurological complications of diabetes.
Chana Dal (split Bengal gram)	Whole or extract of sprouted dal.	Half a cup daily.	Utilizes sugar in the body and reduces the intake of external insulin.
Low fat curds and buttermilk	Buttermilk (chaas), raita or in cooking.	One to two cups daily.	Lactic acid present in these fermented products stimulates the pancreas to produce insulin and hence helps to control blood sugar levels.

Common Myths about Diabetes

Myth Diabetes cannot be prevented...

Fact Diabetes can be prevented, if you do not have a family history of it. Its onset can also be delayed in individuals who have a family history of diabetes and are predisposed to this condition. For example, a WHO report says that if both parents are diabetic there is 99% chance of the child being diabetic, 70% if one parent is diabetic and the other is from a diabetic family, 40% if only one parent is diabetic and only 20% if anyone in the family is diabetic. *Eating regular meals, exercising regularly, refraining from cigarettes and alcohol and keeping stress away are all good measures that can help to keep diabetes away.*

Myth Excessive consumption of sweets can cause diabetes...

Fact Consumption of sugar or sweets is not directly responsible for the onset of diabetes. *It is the body's inability to produce insulin that causes diabetes.* When the cells cannot utilize the sugar or starch we eat, our blood sugar levels rise rapidly causing diabetes or even aggravating already existing diabetes.

However, excessive consumption of sweets can lead to weight gain and such weight gain along with sedentary habits, stress and/or a family history of diabetes can increase the risk of its occurrence.

Myth Diabetes is curable...

Fact There is no real *cure* for diabetes and it is a condition that can be managed through diet control, exercise and medication under the supervision of a physician or diabetologist.

However, if one is a borderline diabetic, with proper care, he can keep the blood sugar levels under control without the use of any medication.

Myth Diabetics should not eat fruits....

Fact It is a false notion that diabetics should not have fruits. One can consume **fibre-rich fruits** like sweet lime, orange, guava, amla, etc. and fruits that are high in water like watermelon, muskmelon, strawberries, papaya, plums etc. as these help to control blood sugar levels. *Due to their low glycemic index, they promote a gradual increase in the blood sugar levels which is beneficial to diabetics.* Fresh fruits like oranges, sweet lime, apples also contribute substantially in providing vitamins and minerals to our diet.

On the other hand, restrict all fruit juices because they contain too much sugar and because plenty of fruit is required to make 1 glass of juice. Juice will also not add any fibre to your diet as most of it is lost in straining thus raising the blood sugar levels instantaneously. Fruits like mango, chickoo, custard apple and grapes should also be restricted as they have a high sugar content. Refer to the Food Exchange List, page 29, to see how much quantity of a particular fruit is allowed.

Myth **Diabetics cannot eat rice .....**

Fact That's not completely true. The caloric value of rice is very close to other cereals like wheat and jowar but rice has a tendency to increase the blood sugar levels very quickly due to its high glycemic index. *Therefore rice should always be combined with some other food, preferably vegetables or dals, as they have a high fibre content which prevents a rapid rise in blood sugar levels.* Brown rice or unpolished rice are better choices as compared to white polished rice as they have more fibre.

Myth **Diabetics can never eat sweets or desserts....**

Fact That's not true. *Diabetics can enjoy an occasional treat like a pastry or an ice-cream but the key is to have it in moderation and also in accordance with the food exchange list on page 29.* If you indulge in a dessert, try and compensate for that treat with other foods in the same meal. For example, if you know you want to eat dessert, then skip either the appetizer or the rice dish.

If you're having dessert, try and share it with someone so that you're not obliged to finish the whole portion. Choose a fruit based dessert over a cream based one.

Try the low calorie desserts that we have made with low fat products and artificial sweeteners, pages 143 to 151, and satiate your sweet tooth.

Myth Artificial sweeteners have no side effects...

Fact *Artificial sweeteners are safe for everyone except pregnant or breast feeding women.* Artificial sweeteners like saccharine and aspartame are almost free of calories and carbohydrates and so do not raise the blood sugar levels like sugar does. Some sweeteners can cause mild reactions like dizziness, headaches, gas or diarrhoea.

Adding it in the right quantity is also vital because if you add too much sweetner, then there is a predominant bitter after taste.

Myth Sugar free products are always safe to consume...

Fact No, this may not apply to every product. Some products that are labelled "sugar free" may be high in fat and hence are not very healthy for diabetics. So it is a good practice to read the nutrition facts on the package before buying any food. Look for *sugar free* and *fat free* on the labels and also consult your diabetologist or nutritionist before consuming such products. Sometimes "sugar free" labels also mean that there's no "added sugar", but the natural sugar may be present eg. Date Mithai or many other dried fruit sweets. Labels can be misleading, so please read the fine print carefully and be cautious.

Abbreviations :

The table below lists the abbreviations used in this book.

ABBREVIATIONS	
CHO	Carbohydrates
F.ACID	Folic acid
VIT.A	Vitamin A
VIT.C	Vitamin C
AMT	Amount
gm	Grams
kcal	Kilocalories
kg	Kilograms
mcg	Micrograms
mg	Milligrams
ml	Millilitres
mg/dl	Milligram per decilitre

Standard Measures:

All the recipes and nutritional values are based on standard cup and spoon measures. They are :

STANDARD MEASURES	
1 cup	200 ml
1 teaspoon	5 ml
1 tablespoon	15 ml

Indian Flavours

Mint and Masoor Tikkis

Prep. time :

10 minutes.

Cooking time :

25 minutes.

Makes 6 tikkis.

An interesting way of combining an unusual leafy vegetable like mint and a pulse like masoor. As I have used only 1 teaspoon of oil to cook these tikkis, they are really amazing being moreover in terms of calories as compared to the deep fried tikkis which are loaded with oil.

Serve these protein, vitamin A and iron rich tikkis as a starter or as a snack during the day.

¼ *cup whole masoor (whole red lentils)*
¼ *cup mint, finely chopped*
1 teaspoon ginger-green chilli paste
2 teaspoons whole wheat bread crumbs
2 tablespoons low fat paneer, page 154, grated
salt to taste

Other ingredients
1 teaspoon oil for cooking

1 Clean, wash and soak the masoor overnight. Drain.
2 Combine the masoor with 2 cups of water and pressure cook till the masoor is soft and slightly overcooked, but not mashed.
3 Drain the masoor and discard any excess water. Coarsely pound the masoor in a mortar and pestle.
4 Combine the masoor paste with the remaining ingredients and mix well.
5 Divide the mixture into 6 equal portions. Shape each portion into an even sized round and flatten the rounds to make tikkis.
6 Heat a non-stick pan and cook each tikki over a high flame using a little oil until both sides are golden brown in colour.
   Serve hot.

Handy tip : Use the discarded masoor dal water to make chapati dough, as it is rich in plenty of nutrients.

AMT	ENERGY	PROTEIN	CHO	FAT	VIT.A	VIT.C	CALCIUM	IRON	F.ACID	FIBRE
gm	kcal	gm	gm	gm	mcg	mg	mg	mg	mcg	gm
12	41	2.7	5.7	0.9	48.5	0.5	35.1	0.8	4.1	0.1

Exchange list per tikki :

CEREAL	PULSE	VEGETABLE	FRUIT	MILK	FAT
—	¼	—	—	—	¼

≈ Hara Bhara Kebabs ≈

Prep. time :

10 minutes.

Cooking time :

20 minutes.

Makes 6 kebabs.

A healthy vegetarian version of kebabs with a tasty blend of ingredients. The spinach adds to its vitamin A content while contributing very little to the carbohydrate levels. The green peas add bulk and fibre to this dish.

Roll these kebabs in whole wheat bread crumbs to make them more nourishing than those coated with refined flour (maida) bread crumbs or rava.

Serve hot.

2 tablespoons chana dal (split Bengal gram)
12 mm. (½") piece ginger, grated
2 cloves garlic, grated
2 green chillies, finely chopped
½ cup spinach (palak), blanched, drained and roughly chopped
¼ cup green peas, boiled
¼ cup low fat paneer, page 154, grated
½ teaspoon chaat masala
¼ teaspoon garam masala
salt to taste

Other ingredients
3 tablespoons whole wheat bread crumbs
1 teaspoon oil for cooking

49

1   Pressure cook the chana dal, ginger, garlic and green chillies with ¾ cup of water for 2 to 3 whistles or until the dal is cooked. Drain out and discard any excess water.
2   Combine the spinach, green peas and cooked dal mixture and blend to a coarse paste without using any water.
3   Add the paneer, chaat masala and garam masala and mix well.
4   Divide the mixture into 6 equal portions and shape them into flat kebabs.
5   Roll the kebabs in the bread crumbs.
6   Heat the oil in a non-stick pan and cook the kebabs on both sides till they are golden brown in colour.
    Serve hot.

✒ Nutritive values per kebab : ✒

AMT	ENERGY	PROTEIN	CHO	FAT	VIT.A	VIT.C	CALCIUM	IRON	F.ACID	FIBRE
gm	kcal	gm	gm	gm	mcg	mg	mg	mg	mcg	gm
50	68	4.1	9.8	1.4	1600.2	8.7	78.4	0.9	43.2	0.5

Exchange list per kebab :

CEREAL	PULSE	VEGETABLE	FRUIT	MILK	FAT		CEREAL	PULSE	VEGETABLE	FRUIT	MILK	FAT
—	¼	½	—	¼	¼	OR	—	—	½	—	½	¼

Mooli ka Salad

Prep. time :

5 minutes.

No Cooking.

Serves 2.

Thickly grated radish is perked up by the addition of an unusual combination of ingredients like garlic, mustard seeds and lemon juice. This makes a tongue tickling dish that is low in calories and carbohydrates and so is a perfect accompaniment to a main course for like khichdi or parathas.

1 cup radish (mooli), thickly grated
1 clove garlic, grated
juice of ½ lemon
½ green chilli, finely chopped
¼ teaspoon split mustard seeds (rai na kuria)
1 teaspoon chopped coriander
salt to taste

1 Combine all the ingredients and allow them to marinate for at least an hour.
2 Cover and refrigerate.
Serve chilled.

Nutritive values per serving :

AMT	ENERGY	PROTEIN	CHO	FAT	VIT. A	VIT. C	CALCIUM	IRON	F.ACID	FIBRE
gm	kcal	gm	gm	gm	mcg	mg	mg	mg	mcg	gm
62	14	0.5	2.7	0.1	36.2	11.7	25.1	0.2	0.0	0.6

Exchange list per serving :

CEREAL	PULSE	VEGETABLE	FRUIT	MILK	FAT
–	–	½	–	–	–

Handy tip : Radish emits a strong odour, so remember to cover the bowl tightly and or plastic wrap so that the other foods in the refrigerator do not smell like radish too.

Fruity Chana Salad

Picture on page 76

Prep. time :

10 minutes.

Cooking time :

20 minutes.

Serves 4.

I often turn to this delightful salad when I have leftover chick peas and a basket of fruits in the refrigerator. The chick peas have a wealth of nutrients like energy, protein, calcium and iron while the orange segments abound in vitamin C which helps to enhance our resistance to diseases.

Feel free to replace orange and pomegranate or with fruits that are handy or fruits you love the most, taking care to avoid ones like mangoes, bananas etc.

Serve this salad with a light main course at lunch time and watch your loved one's relish it.

1 cup cooked chick peas (approx. ½ cup raw chick peas)
½ cup cucumber, sliced
½ cup orange segments, peeled
½ cup onion, sliced
½ cup lettuce, torn
½ cup tomato, sliced
1 tablespoon chopped coriander
1½ teaspoons lemon juice
salt and freshly ground pepper to taste

1 Combine all the ingredients except the salt and pepper and chill.
2 Just before serving, add salt and pepper and mix well.
   Serve chilled.

Handy tip : You can also use rajma (kidney beans) in place of the chick peas, if you like.

Nutritive values per serving :

AMT	ENERGY	PROTEIN	CHO	FAT	VIT. A	VIT. C	CALCIUM	IRON	F.ACID	FIBRE
gm	kcal	gm	gm	gm	mcg	mg	mg	mg	mcg	gm
65	90	3.8	16.1	1.2	281.6	9.1	52.1	1.1	40.7	1.0

Exchange list per per serving :

CEREAL	PULSE	VEGETABLE	FRUIT	MILK	FAT
–	½	–	1	–	–

~ Jamun Raita ~

Prep. time :

15 minutes.

No Cooking.

Serves 4.

Try and have at least a few of these fruits when they are in season for their medicinal value, if not for their unusual flavour.

Jamun is a fruit that is most commonly avoided by many, due to its sharp and tangy taste. However, this fruit is said to be a boon for diabetics as the enzyme *'jamboline' in it helps to control the blood sugar levels. So I've specially made this raita in which the taste of jamun is very nicely enhanced by the blend of cumin powder and coriander with low fat curds. Select sweet and ripe jamuns that are soft and pulpy, for best results.*

Serve this raita with a pulao or even as a dip with fat free khakhras.

½ cup ripe black jamuns, deseeded and finely chopped
1 cup low fat curds, page 153, beaten
½ teaspoon roasted cumin (jeera) powder
1 tablespoon chopped coriander
salt to taste

1 Combine the jamuns, cumin powder, coriander and salt and mix well. Leave aside for 10 to 15 minutes.
2 Add the curds, mix well and refrigerate till chilled. Serve chilled.

Handy tip : You can also make this raita using other fruits like black grapes or pomegranate.

~ Nutritive values per serving : ~

AMT	ENERGY	PROTEIN	CHO	FAT	VIT.A	VIT.C	CALCIUM	IRON	F.ACID	FIBRE
gm	kcal	gm	gm	gm	mcg	mg	mg	mg	mcg	gm
30	33	2.1	6.1	0.1	29.3	5.1	72.7	0.2	0.0	0.0

Exchange list per serving :

CEREAL	PULSE	VEGETABLE	FRUIT	MILK	FAT
–	–	–	¼	¼	–

Karela Theplas

Prep. time :

5 minutes.

Cooking time :

15 minutes.

Makes 10 theplas.

The first thing we all can think about karelas is their bitterness. Believe it or not, karela is a vegetable that is extremely beneficial for diabetics and one can enjoy it more if we acquire the taste for it. This innovative recipe makes use of the peel of the karela which we usually throw away. Wash and chop the peel into small pieces before adding it into the dough. Use the karelas to make the Karela Kadhi, page 71.

1 cup whole wheat flour (gehun ka atta)
¼ cup bajra flour (black millet flour)
½ cup karela peels (bitter gourd), finely chopped
½ teaspoon grated garlic
½ teaspoon turmeric powder (haldi)
1 teaspoon chilli powder
1 teaspoon coriander (dhania) powder
1 tablespoon chopped coriander
salt to taste

Other ingredients
2 teaspoons oil to brush the theplas

1 Combine all the ingredients and knead into a firm dough using enough water and knead well.
2 Divide the dough into 10 equal parts and roll each portion into a circle of approx. 125 mm. (5") diameter.
3 Cook each thepla on a non-stick pan till both sides are golden brown.
4 Brush each thepla with a little oil and serve hot.

❧ Nutritive values per thepla : ❧

AMT	ENERGY	PROTEIN	CHO	FAT	VIT.A	VIT.C	CALCIUM	IRON	F.ACID	FIBRE
gm	kcal	gm	gm	gm	mcg	mg	mg	mg	mcg	gm
20	56	1.7	9.4	1.3	43.1	5.3	7.9	0.8	5.0	0.3

Bajra Turnovers

Prep. time :

10 minutes.

Cooking time :

20 minutes.

Makes 4.

Nutritious bajra and methi rotis stuffed with a delicately spiced mixture of paneer and tomatoes. Both bajra and methi are iron rich with a wealth of fibre too.

Paneer is a rich source of protein and calcium. Preferably, use fresh home-made paneer made with low calorie milk. If you wish, do not fill the turnovers and just make the jowar and methi rotis ...they are yummy on their own too.

For the dough
1 cup bajra flour (black millet flour)
1 cup fenugreek (methi) leaves, chopped
2 large cloves garlic, chopped
1 tablespoon low fat curds, page 153
salt to taste

To be mixed into a filling
½ cup low fat paneer, page 154, crumbled
1 green chilli, finely chopped
⅛ teaspoon turmeric powder (haldi)
¼ teaspoon kasuri methi (dried fenugreek leaves)
3 tablespoons chopped coriander
1 tomato, finely chopped
salt to taste

Other ingredients
1 teaspoon oil for cooking

For the dough
1 In a blender, lightly crush the fenugreek leaves and the garlic with a little salt.
2 Add to the bajra flour and knead into a soft dough using the curds and hot water.

3 Divide the dough into 4 equal portions and roll out each portion into a circle of approx. 100 mm. to 125 mm. (4" to 5") diameter. If you find in difficult to roll the dough, place each portion between two sheets of plastic and then roll out.

How to proceed

1 Place a portion of the filling mixture on one half of each rolled circle and fold it over to make a semi-circle.

2 Lift the turnover carefully and place it on a non-stick pan. Using a little oil, cook on both sides till they are golden brown. These have to be cooked on a very slow flame as the rotis are thicker and will take a while to cook.

3 Repeat with the remaining dough circles and filling mixture to make 3 more turnovers.

Serve hot.

Handy tip : You can make only the bajra rotis using the garlic flavoured dough.

≈ Nutritive values per turnover : ∽

AMT	ENERGY	PROTEIN	CHO	FAT	VIT. A	VIT. C	CALCIUM	IRON	F.ACID	FIBRE
gm	kcal	gm	gm	gm	mcg	mg	mg	mg	mcg	gm
66	149	7.9	23.5	2.6	430.8	12.5	213.9	2.4	16.8	0.5

Exchange list per turnover :

CEREAL	PULSE	VEGETABLE	FRUIT	MILK	FAT
½	–	–	–	1	¼

Lemon Cheesecake, *page 146.*

Green Pea Parathas

Prep. time :

10 minutes.

Cooking time :

15 minutes.

Makes 5 parathas.

Parathas are sustaining and wholesome. Puréed green peas are combined with whole wheat flour to make this delicious paratha dough. Both whole wheat flour and green peas are rich in fibre which aids in controlling the blood sugar levels. Each paratha being cooked in ¼ teaspoon of oil is absolutely healthy for diabetics as well as the whole family.

These parathas taste best when they are served as soon as they are prepared. Serve them with the Karela Kadhi, page 71, and Carrot Garlic Chutney, page 86.

½ cup whole wheat flour (gehun ka atta)
½ cup green peas, boiled
1 to 2 green chillies, finely chopped
1 tablespoon low fat curds, page 153
⅛ teaspoon ajwain (carom seeds)
salt to taste

Other ingredients
1 teaspoon oil for cooking

1 Purée the green peas into a smooth paste in a blender.
2 Combine all the ingredients and knead into a soft dough using enough water.
3 Divide the dough into 5 equal portions.
4 Roll out each portion into a 125 mm. (5") diameter circle with the help of a little flour to roll the paratha.
5 Cook each paratha on a non-stick pan until both sides are golden brown, using a little oil.
Serve hot.

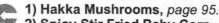

1) Hakka Mushrooms, *page 95.*
2) Spicy Stir Fried Baby Corn, *page 96.*

AMT	ENERGY	PROTEIN	CHO	FAT	VIT.A	VIT.C	CALCIUM	IRON	F.ACID	FIBRE
gm	kcal	gm	gm	gm	mcg	mg	mg	mg	mcg	gm
26	60	2.4	9.9	1.2	23.8	1.3	12.1	0.7	5.1	0.8

Exchange list per paratha :

CEREAL	PULSE	VEGETABLE	FRUIT	MILK	FAT
¼	—	1	—	—	¼

∾ Paneer Khulchas ∾

Prep. time :

15 minutes.

Cooking time :

20 minutes.

Makes 5 khulchas.

Khulchas are always associated with refined flour (maida), but here's one healthy version made with whole wheat flour. Low fat paneer has been used which provides very negligible amount of fat and also enriches these khulchas with protein and calcium. Another speciality of this recipe is that all the khulchas are cooked only in 1 teaspoon of oil. Serve them hot off the tava along with Carrot Methi Subzi, page 70.
You can also use a sautéed onion filling instead of the paneer to make Onion Khulchas.

For the khulcha dough
1 cup whole wheat flour (gehun ka atta)
1 teaspoon (5 grams) fresh yeast, crumbled
a pinch sugar
½ teaspoon salt

To be mixed into a paneer stuffing
½ cup low fat paneer, page 154, crumbled
1 green chilli, finely chopped
¼ teaspoon turmeric powder (haldi)
¼ teaspoon kasuri methi (dried fenugreek leaves)
3 tablespoons chopped coriander
salt to taste

For the khulcha dough

1 Dissolve the yeast and sugar in 2 tablespoons of lukewarm water and leave aside for 10 minutes or until the yeast begins to ferment.
2 Combine all the ingredients in a bowl and knead into a soft dough, using enough water until it is smooth and elastic (approx. 5 to 7 minutes).
3 Cover the dough with a wet muslin cloth and allow it to prove till it doubles in volume (approx. 15 to 20 minutes).
4 Press the dough lightly to remove the air.
5 Divide the dough into 5 equal portions. Keep aside.

How to proceed

1 Roll out one portion of the khulcha dough into a 50 mm. (2") diameter circle.
2 Place one portion of the paneer stuffing in the centre of the circle.
3 Bring together all the sides in the centre and seal tightly.
4 Roll out again into a circle of 150 mm. (6") diameter with the help of a little flour.
5 Cook on a non-stick pan, using a little oil, until both sides are golden brown. The khulchas should puff up like phulkas.
6 Repeat with the remaining dough and stuffing to make 4 more khulchas. Serve immediately.

Handy tips : **1)** You can use ½ teaspoon of dried yeast dissolved in lukewarm water instead of fresh yeast for the above recipe.
2) If the dough is fermenting quickly, refrigerate it till you require it.

Nutritive values per khulcha :

AMT	ENERGY	PROTEIN	CHO	FAT	VIT.A	VIT.C	CALCIUM	IRON	F.ACID	FIBRE
gm	kcal	gm	gm	gm	mcg	mg	mg	mg	mcg	gm
35	118	6.3	20.1	1.4	139.8	2.9	139.9	1.3	7.7	0.4

Exchange list per khulcha :

CEREAL	PULSE	VEGETABLE	FRUIT	MILK	FAT
½	–	–	–	½	¼

Gavar Pumpkin Vegetable

Prep. time :

10 minutes.

Cooking time :

25 minutes.

Serves 4.

Cluster beans are good for diabetics as they have the highest fibre content among all vegetables which in turn prevents a rapid rise in blood sugar levels after a meal.

Red pumpkin has been added to thicken the gravy and it also imparts a natural sweetness to this dish, which is delectable.

You could have never tried this combination of vegetables, but do not hesitate to do so now as this will definitely please your palate.

2 cups cluster beans (gavarfali), cut into 1" pieces
2 cups red pumpkin (kaddu)
1 teaspoon cumin seeds (jeera)
½ teaspoon ajwain (carom seeds)
¼ teaspoon asafoetida (hing)
1 teaspoon chilli powder
½ teaspoon turmeric powder (haldi)
1½ teaspoons crushed garlic
1 tablespoon chopped coriander
1 teaspoon oil
salt to taste

1 Heat the oil in a non-stick pan and add the cumin seeds. When they crackle, add the ajwain and asafoetida.
2 Add the cluster beans, pumpkin, chilli powder, turmeric powder and salt and sauté for 2 to 3 minutes.
3 Add 2 cups of water and bring to a boil.
4 Add the garlic, cover and simmer for 20 minutes or till the cluster beans are cooked.
5 Mash the pumpkin to make a gravy and serve hot, garnished with the chopped coriander.

Handy tip : You can also make this vegetable in a pressure cooker as gavarfali takes a while to cook.

AMT	ENERGY	PROTEIN	CHO	FAT	VIT.A	VIT.C	CALCIUM	IRON	F.ACID	FIBRE
gm	kcal	gm	gm	gm	mcg	mg	mg	mg	mcg	gm
115	35	2.5	8.3	1.5	193.6	26.8	72.7	0.8	80.2	2.1

Exchange list per serving :

CEREAL	PULSE	VEGETABLE	FRUIT	MILK	FAT
–	–	1	–	–	¼

Stuffed Karelas in Makhani Gravy

Prep. time :

20 minutes.

Cooking time :

60 minutes.

Serves 4.

Karela is a low calorie vegetable which is acclaimed for its anti-diabetic properties. This recipe is an attempt to make them appealing. The karelas are stuffed with moong dal and served in a makhani gravy that is made using very little oil.

Enriched with protein, calcium, vitamin A, vitamin C, calcium, iron and fibre, this recipe is a delectable way to savour this *"not so popular"* vegetable.

For the stuffed karelas
4 medium karelas (bitter gourd)
½ cup yellow moong dal (split yellow gram), soaked for 2 hours and drained
¼ teaspoon cumin seeds (jeera)
1 green chilli, chopped
½ teaspoon grated ginger
¼ teaspoon turmeric powder (haldi)
salt to taste
½ teaspoon oil
¼ cup chopped coriander

For the makhani gravy
3 medium tomatoes, sliced
1 medium onion, sliced

2 large cloves garlic, chopped
12 mm. (½") piece ginger, chopped
2 cloves (laung)
1 stick cinnamon (dalchini)
¼ cup red pumpkin (kaddu), chopped
½ teaspoon cumin seeds (jeera)
¼ teaspoon kasuri methi (dried fenugreek leaves)
1 teaspoon chilli powder
½ cup low fat milk, page 152
½ teaspoon cornflour
1 teaspoon oil
salt to taste

For the stuffed karelas

1 Peel the karelas and keep the peels aside for use in another recipe (Karela Theplas, page 54).
2 Slit each one lengthwise. Using a sharp knife, scoop out the insides carefully creating a hollow in the centre. Apply a little salt to the inside and outside of the karelas and keep aside for 10 to 15 minutes.
3 Heat the oil in a non-stick pan and add the cumin seeds. When they crackle, add the soaked moong dal, green chilli, ginger, turmeric powder and salt and mix well.
4 Add ½ cup of water, cover and allow the dal to cook on a slow flame till it is soft and sticky.
5 Add the coriander leaves and mix well. Cool a little.
6 Fill this mixture into the karelas and steam them for 10 to 15 minutes till they are tender. Cut each karela into 2 and keep aside.

For the makhani gravy

1 Combine the tomatoes, onion, garlic, ginger, cloves, cinnamon and red pumpkin with ¾ cup of water and cook over a slow flame till the tomatoes and pumpkin are soft. Allow to cool completely and remove the cloves and cinnamon and discard them.
2 Blend the mixture into a smooth purée.
3 Heat the oil in a non-stick pan and add the cumin seeds.
4 When they crackle, add the puréed tomato mixture, kasuri methi, chilli powder and salt and simmer for 5 to 7 minutes.

5 Dissolve the cornflour in the milk and add it to the prepared gravy. Simmer for a few minutes.

How to proceed
Place the steamed karelas on a serving plate and pour the hot makhani gravy over it.
Serve hot with chapatis.

❧ Nutritive values per serving : ❦

AMT	ENERGY	PROTEIN	CHO	FAT	VIT.A	VIT.C	CALCIUM	IRON	F.ACID	FIBRE
gm	kcal	gm	gm	gm	mcg	mg	mg	mg	mcg	gm
186	135	7.7	20.7	2.4	331.5	85.2	101.9	1.8	46.6	1.4

Exchange list per serving :

CEREAL	PULSE	VEGETABLE	FRUIT	MILK	FAT		CEREAL	PULSE	VEGETABLE	FRUIT	MILK	FAT
–	½	2	–	¼	¼	OR	–	¾	2	–	–	¼

◈ Turai Onion Vegetable ◈

Prep. time :
10 minutes.

Cooking time :
25 minutes.

Serves 4.

Turai, a vegetable that is low in calories and carbohydrates, is combined with onion and flavoured with ginger and garlic to make a simple dish ideal for those of us who like simple flavours. Though the recipe says to use peeled turai, feel free to use them unpeeled to take advantage of the fibre content present in the peels.
Serve this dish with hot phulkas and a salad.

2 cups turai (ridge gourd), peeled and sliced
1 cup onions, sliced
½ teaspoon cumin seeds (jeera)
1 teaspoon chopped ginger
1 teaspoon chopped garlic
1 green chilli, chopped
½ cup yellow moong dal (split yellow gram), soaked and drained

¼ teaspoon turmeric powder (haldi)
1 cup tomatoes, chopped
1½ teaspoons oil
salt to taste

For the garnish
1 tablespoon chopped coriander

1 Heat the oil in a non-stick pan and add the cumin seeds.
2 When they crackle, add the onions and sauté till they are lightly browned.
3 Add the ginger, garlic, green chilli and turai, mix well and sauté for 2 to 3 minutes.
4 Add the moong dal, turmeric powder, salt and approx. ½ cup of water.
5 Cover and cook over a medium flame till the turai and dal are soft.
6 Add the tomatoes and mix well.
7 Simmer for another 4 to 5 minutes till the tomatoes soften.
    Serve hot garnished with the chopped coriander.

Nutritive values per serving :

AMT	ENERGY	PROTEIN	CHO	FAT	VIT.A	VIT.C	CALCIUM	IRON	F.ACID	FIBRE
gm	kcal	gm	gm	gm	mcg	mg	mg	mg	mcg	gm
123	106	5.4	16.1	2.2	178.9	14.6	48.6	1.3	39.2	0.8

Exchange list per serving :

CEREAL	PULSE	VEGETABLE	FRUIT	MILK	FAT
–	½	2	–	–	¼

Dhan-saak Dal

Prep. time :

25 minutes.

Cooking time :

30 minutes.

Makes 4.

A traditional Parsi dish. As the name says, it is an interesting combination of five varieties of dhan (dals) and saak (vegetables) perked with spices to give it a mouth watering taste.

Being loaded with vegetables, this dish is not very high in calories and carbohydrates and also provides all the necessary nutrients. Serve it with crusty whole wheat bread and salad to make a light, yet satisfying meal.

½ cup toovar (arhar) dal
2 teaspoons moong dal (split yellow gram)
2 teaspoons masoor dal (split red lentils)
2 teaspoons urad dal (split black lentils)
2 teaspoons val dal
¼ cup potato, chopped
¼ cup brinjal, chopped
¼ cup bottle gourd (doodhi / lauki), chopped
¼ cup red pumpkin (kaddu), chopped
1 spring onion, chopped
1 tablespoon fenugreek (methi) leaves, chopped
1 tomato, chopped
3 teaspoons tamarind, soaked in ¼ cup of water
1 teaspoon oil
salt to taste

To be ground into a paste
1 green chilli
3 red chillies
4 cloves garlic
1 stick cinnamon (dalchini)
4 cloves (laung)
25 mm. (1") piece ginger
1 cardamom (elaichi)
1 teaspoon coriander (dhania) seeds
4 peppercorns

½ teaspoon cumin seeds (jeera)
2 teaspoons chopped coriander
2 tablespoons water

To be made into a dry powdered masala
1 cardamom (elaichi)
1 cinnamon (dalchini)
1 clove (laung)

1 Combine the dals and wash them.
2 Add the vegetables to the dals along with 3 cups of water and pressure cook for 3 whistles.
3 Liquidise the cooked dals and all the vegetables in a blender and keep aside.
4 Heat the oil in a non-stick pan and add the ground paste. Sauté it for 4 to 5 minutes and add the puréed vegetable and dal mixture, along with the dry powdered masala, tamarind water and salt. Simmer for 10 to 15 minutes. Serve hot, with whole wheat bread or chapatis.

❧ Nutritive values per serving : ❧

AMT	ENERGY	PROTEIN	CHO	FAT	VIT.A	VIT.C	CALCIUM	IRON	F.ACID	FIBRE
gm	kcal	gm	gm	gm	mcg	mg	mg	mg	mcg	gm
88	127	7.2	20.5	1.8	177.3	9.4	43.9	1.2	37.8	0.8

Exchange list per serving :

CEREAL	PULSE	VEGETABLE	FRUIT	MILK	FAT		CEREAL	PULSE	VEGETABLE	FRUIT	MILK	FAT
—	½	2½	—	—	¼	OR	—	¾	1½	—	—	¼

Handy tip : You can also use ready made Dhan-saak Masala available at most grocery stores instead of all the spices used, if you are in a hurry.

Khumb Hara Dhania

Prep. time :

15 minutes.

Cooking time :

30 minutes.

Serves 4.

Mushrooms are called khumb in Hindi. They are mildly flavoured vegetables that absorb other flavours beautifully to make a tempting dish each time. Whether it is with tomatoes and oregano or spinach, onions and garlic, they make a delectable dish in all combinations.

This recipe is mildly flavoured with coriander and an array of delicate spices to create a lip smacking dish that is rich in protein, calcium, vitamin A and iron. It is an unusual delicacy to enjoy, especially if you're entertaining.

2 cups mushrooms, cut into quarters and blanched
½ cup chopped coriander
½ teaspoon cumin seeds (jeera)
¼ teaspoon kasuri methi (dried fenugreek leaves)
¼ cup low fat milk, page 152
¼ cup low fat curds, page 153
½ teaspoon Bengal gram flour (besan)
¼ teaspoon garam masala
1 teaspoon oil
salt to taste

For the paste
1¼ cups sliced onions
¼ cup cauliflower, finely chopped
1 to 2 green chillies
12 mm. (½") piece ginger, sliced
1 stick cinnamon (dalchini)
1 clove (laung)
1 cup low fat milk, page 152

For the paste
1 Combine all the ingredients in a pan and simmer for 8 to 10 minutes till the onions are soft and nearly all the liquid has evaporated. Cool.
2 Purée the mixture to a smooth paste in a blender. Keep aside.

How to proceed
1 Combine the milk, curds and gram flour and mix well. Keep aside.

2 Heat the oil in a non-stick pan, add the cumin seeds, kasuri methi and the prepared paste and sauté for 2 to 3 minutes.

3 Add the curds and gram flour mixture, garam masala and salt and bring to a boil.

4 Add the mushrooms and coriander and mix well.
Serve hot.

Nutritive values per serving :

AMT	ENERGY	PROTEIN	CHO	FAT	VIT.A	VIT.C	CALCIUM	IRON	F.ACID	FIBRE
gm	kcal	gm	gm	gm	mcg	mg	mg	mg	mcg	gm
69	60	4.1	8.0	1.5	220.5	10.2	120.4	0.7	8.7	0.6

Exchange list per serving :

CEREAL	PULSE	VEGETABLE	FRUIT	MILK	FAT
–	–	1	–	¼	¼

Carrot Methi Subzi

Prep. time :

10 minutes.

Cooking time :

15 minutes.

Serves 4.

This is a great combination of textures and fragrant, spicy flavours that has the added advantage of being quick to make. Enriched with vitamin A, iron and fibre, it is nutritious too.

Paneer Khulchas, page 60, are the perfect accompaniment to this dish. Alternatively, just serve the subzi with hot phulkas.

2 cups carrots, cut into cubes
2 cups fenugreek (methi) leaves, chopped
½ teaspoon cumin seeds (jeera)
1 large onion, finely chopped
3 to 4 green chillies, finely chopped
1 large clove garlic, finely chopped
12 mm. (½") piece ginger, finely chopped
¼ teaspoon turmeric powder (haldi)
2 teaspoons coriander (dhania) powder
2 teaspoons oil
salt to taste

1 Heat the oil in a non-stick pan and add the cumin seeds.
2 When they crackle, add the onion, green chillies, garlic and ginger and sauté for 2 minutes.
3 Add the fenugreek leaves and sauté another 2 minutes.
4 Add the carrots, turmeric powder, coriander powder, salt and 1 cup of water and stir.
5 Cover and cook over a slow flame till all the moisture has evaporated and the carrots are tender.

Serve hot, with the paneer khulchas.

❧ Nutritive values per serving : ❧

AMT	ENERGY	PROTEIN	CHO	FAT	VIT.A	VIT.C	CALCIUM	IRON	F.ACID	FIBRE
gm	kcal	gm	gm	gm	mcg	mg	mg	mg	mcg	gm
69	55	1.2	6.6	2.7	879.3	10.8	89.3	0.7	5.7	0.6

Exchange list per serving :

CEREAL	PULSE	VEGETABLE	FRUIT	MILK	FAT
–	–	1½	–	–	¼

❧ Karela Kadhi ❧

Prep. time :
10 minutes.

Cooking time :
15 minutes.

Serves 4.

Another karela delicacy—an innovative calcium rich kadhi! Keep in mind however that the karelas must be well cooked before adding the curds and spices to remove most of its bitterness. Enjoy its unusual flavours with Soyabean Biryani, page 78.

¼ cup karelas (bitter gourd), finely chopped
½ cup onions, chopped
1 teaspoon ginger-green chilli paste
1 cup low fat curds, page 153
2 tablespoons Bengal gram flour (besan)
¼ cup chopped coriander
1 teaspoon oil
salt to taste

1 Heat the oil in a non-stick pan, add the onions and sauté for a few minutes.
2 Add the karelas and salt and cook over a medium flame till they are soft.
3 In a bowl, whisk the curds and Bengal gram flour together till they form a smooth paste.
4 Add the ginger-green chilli paste and the gram flour and curds mixture to the sautéed onion and karelas along with 1 cup of water. Bring to a boil while stirring continuously.
5 Adjust the salt and simmer for a few minutes.
   Serve hot, garnished with the coriander.

☙ Nutritive values per serving : ❧

AMT	ENERGY	PROTEIN	CHO	FAT	VIT.A	VIT.C	CALCIUM	IRON	F.ACID	FIBRE
gm	kcal	gm	gm	gm	mcg	mg	mg	mg	mcg	gm
28	55	3.1	7.2	1.5	129.0	10.3	82.6	0.4	6.9	0.2

Exchange list per serving :

CEREAL	PULSE	VEGETABLE	FRUIT	MILK	FAT
–	–	1	–	¼	¼

Varagu and Matki Pulao

Prep. time :

10 minutes.

Cooking time :

25 minutes.

Serves 2.

This sumptuous and simple dish is enlivened with the addition of vegetables and sprouts. Sprouting not only enhances the nutritive value of foods but also makes them easier to digest. It is really easy to make sprouts at home — simply soak the matki in water for 6 to 8 hours and then wrap them in a damp muslin cloth for 2 to 3 days taking care to keep the muslin damp at all times.

Varagu is available at most traditional banias, not at our larger grocery stores. Ask your neighbourhood bania to get you some as it's a good substitute for rice.

Serve with Low Fat Curds, page 153, or Jamun Raita, page 53.

½ cup varagu (kodri)
½ cup matki (moath beans) sprouts
½ teaspoon cumin (jeera) powder
¼ teaspoon asafoetida (hing)
2 cloves (laung)
1 bay leaf
¼ cup onions, chopped
½ cup carrots, chopped
½ cup french beans, chopped
¼ teaspoon turmeric powder (haldi)
½ teaspoon chilli powder
1 teaspoon coriander (dhania) powder
1 teaspoon oil
salt to taste

1   Heat the oil in a non-stick pan and add the cumin seeds.
2   When they crackle, add the asafoetida, cloves and bay leaf and stir for a few seconds.
3   Add the onions, carrots, french beans and salt and sauté them for 4 to 5 minutes.
4   Add the varagu and matki sprouts along with the turmeric powder, chilli powder and coriander powder and mix well.

5 Add approx. 2½ cups of water, cover and cook over a medium flame till the varagu and matki are cooked.

Serve hot, with low fat curds or jamun raita.

✍ Nutritive values per serving : ✍

AMT	ENERGY	PROTEIN	CHO	FAT	VIT.A	VIT.C	CALCIUM	IRON	F.ACID	FIBRE
gm	kcal	gm	gm	gm	mcg	mg	mg	mg	mcg	gm
53	98	3.4	17.6	1.6	160.7	4.3	34.1.	0.9	11.3	2.2

Exchange list per serving :

CEREAL	PULSE	VEGETABLE	FRUIT	MILK	FAT
¼	¼	1 ½	—	—	¼

❧ Moong and Buckwheat Khichdi ❧

Prep. time :

5 minutes.

Cooking time :

20 minutes.

Serves 6.

Khichdi is light for the stomach, yet filling and nourishing. They often say soup is good for the soul, but I would say, "Khichdi is good for my soul". The aroma of this khichdi is irresistable, as it has been cooked with aromatic spices.

Buckwheat is commonly called as kutto or kutti no daro. This recipe is a variation of traditional khichdi in which rice is replaced with buckwheat due to its low glycemic index and high fibre content.

Serve it with chilled Low Fat Curds, page 153, or Karela Kadhi, page 71, to make a satisfying meal.

½ cup yellow moong dal (split yellow gram)
1½ cups buckwheat (kutto or kutti no daro)

Nourishing Barley Soup, *page 107.*

2 peppercorns
1 to 2 cloves (laung)
½ teaspoon cumin seeds (jeera)
¼ teaspoon asafoetida (hing)
¼ teaspoon turmeric powder (haldi)
1 teaspoon oil
salt to taste

1 Clean and wash the moong dal and buckwheat together. Drain and keep aside.
2 Heat the oil in a pressure cooker and add the peppercorns, cloves and cumin seeds.
3 When the cumin seeds crackle, add the asafoetida, followed by the moong dal and buckwheat and sauté for 2 to 3 minutes.
4 Add the turmeric powder, salt and approx. 4 cups of water and pressure cook for 2 to 3 whistles.
5 Serve hot, with karela kadhi, page 71.

ೞ **Nutritive values per serving :** ೞ

AMT	ENERGY	PROTEIN	CHO	FAT	VIT.A	VIT.C	CALCIUM	IRON	F.ACID	FIBRE
gm	kcal	gm	gm	gm	mcg	mg	mg	mg	mcg	gm
49	165	6.7	30.4	1.8	13.7	0.0	31.9	5.9	17.7	3.1

Exchange list per serving :

CEREAL	PULSE	VEGETABLE	FRUIT	MILK	FAT
½	½	2	—	—	¼

Fruity Chana Salad, page 52.

Soyabean Biryani

Prep. time :

20 minutes.

Cooking time :

½ hour.

Serves 4.

Baking time :

30 minutes.

Baking temperature :

180°C (360°F).

A nutri-packed biryani! Soyabeans are one of the healthiest pulses for a vegetarian diet as apart form other nutrients, they also abound in vitamin B_{12} which is otherwise lacking in other vegetarian foods.

I have added three parts of vegetables to make the glycemic index of this dish lower.

You will surely relish the spicy flavours of the masala mixture in this recipe.

This is a good dish for a packed lunch to take to work that will satiate you and keep you going for a longer period.

½ cup soyabeans, soaked overnight
1 cup cooked rice
1 stick cinnamon (dalchini)
1 cardamom (elaichi)
1 bay leaf
salt to taste

For the masala mixture
½ cup onions, sliced
½ teaspoon cumin seeds (jeera)
1 teaspoon ginger-garlic paste
1 cup tomatoes, chopped
½ teaspoon turmeric powder (haldi)
½ teaspoon chilli powder
½ teaspoon coriander (dhania) powder
¼ cup low fat milk, page 152, or low fat curds, page 153
1½ cups mixed boiled vegetables (peas, french beans, cauliflower)
¼ cup mint, chopped
¼ cup chopped coriander
1 teaspoon oil
salt to taste

1 Wash and drain the soyabeans. Add approx. 2 cups of water and the cinnamon, cardamom, bay leaf and salt and cook over a medium flame till they are cooked. Drain and keep aside.
2 Combine the cooked rice and soyabeans.

For the masala mixture
1 Heat the oil in a non-stick pan and add the cumin seeds.
2 When they crackle, add the onions and ginger-garlic paste and sauté till the onions are lightly browned.
3 Add the tomatoes, turmeric powder, chilli powder, coriander powder and ¼ cup of water and cook till the water evaporates and the tomatoes are soft.
4 Add the milk, salt and boiled vegetables and mix well. Simmer for 5 to 7 minutes till the mixture is semi dry. Then add the coriander and mint leaves.

How to proceed
1 Spread half the rice and soya beans in a 200 mm. (8") diameter baking dish and spoon all the masala mixture on top.
2 Top with the remaining rice and soya beans and cover with aluminum foil.
3 Bake in a pre-heated oven at 180°C (360°F) for 20 to 30 minutes. Serve hot, with low fat curds.

❧ Nutritive values per serving : ❧

AMT	ENERGY	PROTEIN	CHO	FAT	VIT.A	VIT.C	CALCIUM	IRON	F.ACID	FIBRE
gm	kcal	gm	gm	gm	mcg	mg	mg	mg	mcg	gm
112	135	7.5	18.9	3.2	324.1	23.2	77.9	1.8	29.5	1.8

Exchange list per serving :

CEREAL	PULSE	VEGETABLE	FRUIT	MILK	FAT
½	½	1	—	—	¼

Green Pea Pancakes

Prep. time :

30 minutes.

Cooking time :

20 minutes.

Makes 4 pancakes.

Enjoy these crisp yet spongy pancakes early in the morning before starting your day.

The combination of green peas with moong dal helps to enhance the fibre and protein content of this recipe.

Serve hot, with Carrot Garlic Chutney, page 86.

1 cup yellow moong dal (split yellow gram)
1 cup green peas
1 to 2 green chillies
1 teaspoon grated ginger
½ cup chopped onions
1 tablespoon chopped coriander
salt to taste

Other ingredients
1 teaspoon oil for cooking

1   Soak the moong dal in warm water for 30 minutes. Drain.
2   Combine with the peas, chillies and ginger and grind in a blender using enough water to make a thick batter.
3   Pour a quarter of the batter onto a lightly greased non-stick pan to get a pancake of 125 mm. (5") diameter, using a little oil.
4   Cook over a medium flame till both sides are golden brown.
5   Repeat with the remaining batter to make 3 more pancakes.
    Serve hot.

✑ Nutritive values per pancake : ✑

AMT	ENERGY	PROTEIN	CHO	FAT	VIT.A	VIT.C	CALCIUM	IRON	F.ACID	FIBRE
gm	kcal	gm	gm	gm	mcg	mg	mg	mg	mcg	gm
74	168	10.8	27.4	1.7	96.3	4.4	41.1	1.9	55.8	1.1

CEREAL	PULSE	VEGETABLE	FRUIT	MILK	FAT
–	1	2	–	–	¼

Varagu Upma

Prep. time :

10 minutes.

Cooking time :

15 minutes.

Serves 2.

A fibre rich version of upma that is good for a diabetic breakfast. This recipe cooks varagu in yoghurt gravy that is tempered with urad dal and green chillies and other subtle spices.

Varagu is not a very commonly used cereal. It resembles larger grains of rava (semolina), but is healthier than rava since it is unrefined and also has a low glycemic index. Look for it at your neighbourhood grocery store or at a health food store. In case you cannot find it, use bulgur wheat instead.

½ cup varagu (kodri), cleaned and washed
¼ cup onions, finely chopped
¾ cup vegetables (carrot, french beans and peas)
1 teaspoon urad dal (split black lentils)
½ teaspoon mustard seeds (rai)
1 to 2 green chillies
2 to 3 curry leaves
a pinch asafoetida (hing)
1 teaspoon oil
¼ cup low fat curds, page 153, beaten
salt to taste

1   Dry roast the varagu till it is golden brown. Keep aside.
2   Heat the oil in a non-stick pan and add the urad dal, mustard seeds, green chillies and curry leaves.
3   When the mustard seeds crackle, add the asafoetida and onions and sauté till the onions are golden brown in colour.
4   Add the vegetables along with ½ cup of water and cook till they are tender.
5   Add the varagu, salt and 1½ cups of water. Mix well, cover and simmer for 5 to 10 minutes till the varagu is cooked, adding more water if required.
6   Add the curds and mix well.
    Serve hot.

AMT	ENERGY	PROTEIN	CHO	FAT	VIT.A	VIT.C	CALCIUM	IRON	F.ACID	FIBRE
gm	kcal	gm	gm	gm	mcg	mg	mg	mg	mcg	gm
96	178	6.1	31.5	3.1	186.6	6.7	69.9	0.8	20.0	4.3

Exchange list per serving :

CEREAL	PULSE	VEGETABLE	FRUIT	MILK	FAT
1	—	2	—	—	¼

Chana Dal Pancakes

Prep. time :

10 minutes.

Cooking time :

15 minutes.

Makes 4 pancakes.

It has been recently discovered that chana dal is a very beneficial pulse for diabetics as it helps in the utilization of sugar effectively and causes a slow rise in blood sugar levels because of its low glycemic index.

This recipe makes use of soaked chana dal mixed with vitamin rich vegetables and protein rich low fat curds to enhance its taste. Grated ginger and green chillies add the much-needed spice to these pancakes. Cook these pancakes over a slow flame as the chana dal is coarsely ground and will take a while to cook well.

½ cup chana dal (split Bengal gram), soaked and drained
½ cup fenugreek (methi) leaves, chopped
½ cup spinach (palak), chopped
½ cup carrots, grated
4 to 6 curry leaves, chopped
1 tablespoon low fat curds, page 153
1 sachet fruit salt
1 teaspoon grated ginger
1 to 2 green chillies, chopped
salt to taste

Other ingredients
1 teaspoon oil for cooking

1 Grind the soaked chana dal into a coarse paste adding a little water if required

2 Add the fenugreek leaves, spinach, carrot, curry leaves, ginger, green chillies and salt and mix well.

3 Just before serving, add the curds and fruit salt and mix well.

4 Divide the batter into 4 equal portions, spread one portion on a non-stick pan and make a pancake of approx. 125 mm. (5") diameter.

5 Cook on a slow flame till both sides are golden brown, drizzling a little oil if required.

6 Repeat with the remaining batter to make 3 more pancakes. Serve hot.

৯ Nutritive values per pancake : ৩

AMT	ENERGY	PROTEIN	CHO	FAT	VIT.A	VIT.C	CALCIUM	IRON	F.ACID	FIBRE
gm	kcal	gm	gm	gm	mcg	mg	mg	mg	mcg	gm
45	98	4.8	14.1	2.5	801.8	4.8	45.4	1.4	42.3	0.5

Exchange list per pancake :

CEREAL	PULSE	VEGETABLE	FRUIT	MILK	FAT
—	½	1½	—	—	¼

৯ Karela Muthias ৩

Prep. time :

10 minutes.

Cooking time :

20 minutes.

Serves 4.

Karela and flour dumplings that are enlivened with the addition of onions and garlic to make a delicious breakfast. This recipe makes use of karelas and garlic, the two ingredients that are said to be diabetic friendly as they help to maintain the blood sugar levels.

Serve them hot, along with Low Calorie Green Chutney, page 85.

½ cup karelas (bitter gourd), finely chopped, with the peel
⅓ cup onions, chopped
2 large cloves garlic, chopped
1 teaspoon grated ginger
1 to 2 green chillies, chopped
1 tablespoon chopped coriander

½ teaspoon turmeric powder (haldi)
1 tablespoon low fat curds, page 153
¼ cup jowar flour (white millet flour)
¼ cup whole wheat flour (gehun ka atta)
½ cup Bengal gram flour (besan)
⅛ teaspoon soda bi-carb
salt to taste

For the tempering
½ teaspoon cumin seeds (jeera)
¼ teaspoon asafoetida (hing)
1 teaspoon oil

For the garnish
1 tablespoon chopped coriander

1 Combine all the ingredients except the soda bi-carb in a bowl and knead into a soft dough using enough water.
2 Add the soda bi-carb and mix well.
3 Place the dough on a steamer and steam for 10 to 12 minutes or till a knife inserted into the muthia comes out clean.
4 Cool, cut into 25 mm. (1") cubes and keep aside.

For the tempering
1 Heat the oil in a non-stick pan and add the cumin seeds.
2 When they crackle, add the asafoetida and then the pieces of muthia. Sauté them over a medium flame till they are lightly browned.
Serve immediately, garnished with the coriander.

❧ Nutritive values per serving : ❧

AMT	ENERGY	PROTEIN	CHO	FAT	VIT.A	VIT.C	CALCIUM	IRON	F.ACID	FIBRE
gm	kcal	gm	gm	gm	mcg	mg	mg	mg	mcg	gm
51˙	105	4.1	17.4	2.1	150.8	15.7	26.4	1.3	19.4	0.5

Exchange list per serving :

CEREAL	PULSE	VEGETABLE	FRUIT	MILK	FAT
¼	¼	1½	–	–	¼

Low Calorie Green Chutney

Prep. time :

10 minutes.

Cooking time :

2 minutes.

Makes ½ cup

(approx. 7 tablespoons).

Chutneys are a favourite accompaniment for snacks as well for main meals. This low calorie chutney uses chana dal (daria) instead of fat laden ingredients like coconut and peanuts. Curds have been used to retain the fresh green colour of this chutney. It can be stored refrigerated for 2 to 3 days.

½ cup roasted chana dal (daria)
¼ cup chopped coriander
1 green chilli, chopped
1 tablespoon low fat curds, page 153, beaten
salt to taste

For the seasoning
½ teaspoon oil
a pinch of asafoetida (hing)
⅛ teaspoon mustard seeds (rai)

1 Combine the chana dal, coriander and green chilli with 1 cup of water and grind to a smooth paste.
2 For the seasoning, heat the oil, add the asafoetida and mustard seeds and fry until the seeds crackle.
3 Pour the seasoning over the chutney, add the curds and mix well.

Nutritive values per tablespoon :

AMT	ENERGY	PROTEIN	CHO	FAT	VIT.A	VIT.C	CALCIUM	IRON	F.ACID	FIBRE
gm	kcal	gm	gm	gm	mcg	mg	mg	mg	mcg	gm
13`	46	2.5	7.2	0.8	76.0	1.3	11.1	0.6	17.3	0.2

Carrot Garlic Chutney

Prep. time :

30 minutes.

No Cooking.

Makes ½ cup

(approx. 7 tablespoons).

Carrots, garlic, chilli powder and lemon juice are combined to make a tasty accompaniment for rotis, parathas or a spread for sandwiches. Carrots are rich in fibre and vitamin A and the garlic is good to control the sugar and cholesterol levels in the blood. Enjoy this chutney with hot Bajra Turnovers, page 55.

1 cup carrots, thickly grated
2 tablespoons garlic, chopped
2 teaspoons chilli powder
¼ teaspoon lemon juice
1 teaspoon oil
1 teaspoon salt

1 Sprinkle ½ teaspoon of salt on the grated carrots and leave aside for 30 minutes. Drain out the juices.
2 Grind the garlic, chilli powder, lemon juice and the remaining ½ teaspoon of salt to a fine paste in a blender or a mortar and pestle.
3 Combine the carrots, garlic paste and oil in a bowl and mix well. Store refrigerated.

Handy tip : The chutney will stay well if refrigerated for upto 4 days.

❧ Nutritive values per tablespoon : ❧

AMT	ENERGY	PROTEIN	CHO	FAT	VIT.A	VIT.C	CALCIUM	IRON	F.ACID	FIBRE
gm	kcal	gm	gm	gm	mcg	mg	mg	mg	mcg	gm
14	13	0.1	1.4	0.7	244.0	0.7	10.6	0.1	1.9	0.2

Quick Soya Dosas

Prep. time :

5 minutes.

Cooking time :

10 minutes.

Fermentation time :

30 minutes.

Makes 4 dosas.

Try these instant dosas when you want to grab a healthy snack which does not shoot up your blood sugar levels rapidly.

Soyabeans apart from helping in controlling blood sugar levels are a good source of protein and vitamin B_{12} too. It is the best known source of vegetarian protein. Soya flour is ready available at most health food stores.

Serve hot with Low Calorie Green Chutney, page 85.

¾ cup rice flour (chawal ka atta)
¼ cup urad dal (split black lentils) flour
¼ cup soya flour
1 teaspoon fruit salt
salt to taste

Other ingredients
1 teaspoon oil for cooking

1. Mix together the rice flour, urad dal flour, soya flour and salt with approx. 1 cup of water to make a thin batter.
2. Keep aside for 30 minutes.
3. When ready to make the dosas, sprinkle the fruit salt on the batter and mix gently.
4. Heat a non-stick pan and grease it lightly with oil.
5. When hot, pour one quarter of the batter on the pan and spread it using a circular motion to make a thin dosa. Cook on one side and pour a little oil along the edges while cooking. When crispy, fold over.
6. Repeat with the remaining batter to make 3 more dosas.
   Serve hot, with low calorie green chutney.

Nutritive values per dosa :

AMT	ENERGY	PROTEIN	CHO	FAT	VIT.A	VIT.C	CALCIUM	IRON	F.ACID	FIBRE
gm	kcal	gm	gm	gm	mcg	mg	mg	mg	mcg	gm
38	140	5.6	24.1	2.3	33.0	0.0	27.1	1.0	18.6	0.3

Exchange list per dosa :

CEREAL	PULSE	VEGETABLE	FRUIT	MILK	FAT
¾	½	—	—	—	¼

~ Chola Dal Dhoklas ~

Prep. time :

10 minutes.

Cooking time :

15 minutes.

Serves 4.

(Makes 16 pieces).

Dhoklas are a favourite Gujarati snack. Dhoklas are usually made with ground and fermented pulses and are steamed. As they are steamed, they are healthier than most other snacks. The addition of spinach and fenugreek enriches this recipe with vitamin A (that aids in healthy vision) and iron (that is responsible for blood formation).

These quick and easy to make dhoklas are best enjoyed as a breakfast dish or even for a late afternoon snack. They are quicker to make as instead of fermenting the batter overnight, I have used fruit salt for this purpose. Serve hot with Low Calorie Green Chutney, page 85.

½ cup chola dal (split black eyed beans), soaked overnight
½ cup spinach (palak), chopped
½ cup fenugreek (methi) leaves, chopped
2 teaspoons green chilli-ginger paste
¼ teaspoon asafoetida (hing)
1 teaspoon fruit salt
salt to taste

Other ingredients
½ teaspoon oil for greasing

1 Wash and drain the dal and place it in a blender.
2 Add the spinach, fenugreek leaves and green chilli-ginger paste and grind to a paste, adding a little water if required.
3 Add the asafoetida and salt and mix well.
4 Grease a 150 mm. (6") diameter dhokla plate and keep aside.
5 Add the fruit salt, sprinkle a little water over and mix gently.

6 Pour into the greased thali and steam for 8 to 10 minutes or till a skewer inserted comes out clean.

Serve hot, with low calorie green chutney.

❧ **Nutritive values per serving (4 pieces) :** ❧

AMT	ENERGY	PROTEIN	CHO	FAT	VIT.A	VIT.C	CALCIUM	IRON	F.ACID	FIBRE
gm	kcal	gm	gm	gm	mcg	mg	mg	mg	mcg	gm
33	74	5.1	11.3	0.9	564.2	4.2	35.4	1.9	37.1	0.8

Exchange list per serving (4 pieces) :

CEREAL	PULSE	VEGETABLE	FRUIT	MILK	FAT
—	¼	1½	—	—	⅛

❧ *Buttermilk Pancakes* ❧

Prep. time :

5 minutes.

Cooking time :

15 minutes.

Makes 4 pancakes.

Pancakes are an American breakfast dish. I've specially created this recipe as the lactic acid in the curds is known to stimulate the pancreas to produce insulin which helps to control blood sugar levels. The sweet apple topping is a healthier option to the dollop of butter and drizzle of honey that traditionally goes with pancakes. The cinnamon apple topping adds the much needed crunch and sweetness along with the goodness of apples.

For the pancakes
1 cup whole wheat flour (gehun ka atta)
1 cup buttermilk (made from 5 tablespoons low fat curds, page 153)
¼ cup low fat milk, page 152
a pinch salt

For the apple topping
1 cup apples, chopped
¼ teaspoon cinnamon (dalchini) powder
½ sachet sugar substitute

For the apple topping
1 Combine the apple with ¼ cup water in a pan and bring to a boil.
2 Simmer for 5 to 7 minutes till the apples soften.
3 Add the cinnamon powder and the sugar subsitute and mix well.

For the pancakes
1 Combine all the ingredients in a bowl and whisk them together to make a smooth batter. Allow to rest for 10 minutes.
2 Pour a quarter of the batter onto a greased non-stick pan.
3 Cook till both sides are golden brown and serve topped with the apple topping.
4 Repeat to make 3 more pancakes.

Handy tip : Buttermilk is made by whisking together curds and water.

Nutritive values per pancake :

AMT	ENERGY	PROTEIN	CHO	FAT	VIT.A	VIT.C	CALCIUM	IRON	F.ACID	FIBRE
gm	kcal	gm	gm	gm	mcg	mg	mg	mg	mcg	gm
58	117	4.2	23.8	0.6	7.8	0.4	46.7	1.5	9.7	0.8

Exchange list per pancake :

CEREAL	PULSE	VEGETABLE	FRUIT	MILK	FAT
½	–	–	1	¼	–

International Flavours

Baked Tortilla Chips

Prep. time :

10 minutes.

Cooking time :

5 minutes.

**Makes 36 pieces
(6 servings).**

Baking time :

10 minutes.

Baking temperature :

190°C (380°F).

A quick, easy-to-make, healthy starter which is a popular choice in Mexico. The tortillas are *baked and made with minimal oil from a blend of whole wheat flour and maize flour instead of the traditional Mexican tortillas made with refined flour which are also deep fried.*

Whole wheat flour has been used as it abounds in fibre which aids in controlling blood sugar and cholesterol levels.

Eat these chips with tomato salsa and get your taste buds going by enjoying its lively flavours. You can also make a large batch of these at one go and store them in an air-tight container for the contingencies when hunger strikes…unexpectedly.

1 cup maize flour (makai ka atta)
½ cup whole wheat flour (gehun ka atta)
¼ teaspoon chilli powder
¼ teaspoon ajwain (carom seeds)
1 teaspoon oil
salt to taste
flour for dusting

1 Combine all the ingredients in a bowl and knead into a soft dough using hot water.
2 Divide the dough into 6 equal portions.
3 Roll out each portion between two sheets of plastic into a thin circle of 175 mm. (7") diameter. Dust the tortillas generously with flour to make the rolling easier.
4 Lightly cook the tortillas on a non-stick pan.
5 Cut each tortilla into 6 triangular pieces.
6 Place the tortilla pieces in a single layer on a non-stick baking tray.
7 Bake at 190°C (380°F) for 7 to 8 minutes or until the tortilla chips are crisp and lightly browned.
8 Cool and store in an air-tight container.

AMT	ENERGY	PROTEIN	CHO	FAT	VIT. A	VIT. C	CALCIUM	IRON	F.ACID	FIBRE
gm	kcal	gm	gm	gm	mcg	mg	mg	mg	mcg	gm
26	58	1.8	10.1	1.1	15.1	0.9	5.7	0.6	3.2	0.5

Exchange list per serving (6 pieces) :

CEREAL	PULSE	VEGETABLE	FRUIT	MILK	FAT
½	–	–	–	–	–

꒰ Green Tomato Salsa ꒱

Prep. time :

10 minutes.

No Cooking.

Makes 1 cup.

Green tomatoes are blended with spring onions and garlic to provide the necessary flavours to make this healthy dip that is sure to be a hit when you're entertaining. The addition of coriander adds further to its taste while providing vitamins A and C. Enjoy this salsa with Baked Tortilla Chips, page 92, or colourful vegetable crudités.

1 cup green tomatoes, chopped
1 spring onion, chopped
2 cloves garlic
½ teaspoon cumin seeds (jeera), roasted
1 green chilli, chopped
1 tablespoon chopped coriander
salt to taste

1　Combine all the ingredients in a blender and grind into a coarse mixture.
2　Chill and serve with baked tortilla chips.

Handy tip : If the tomatoes are really sharp, add ½ sachet of sugar substitute.

AMT	ENERGY	PROTEIN	CHO	FAT	VIT. A	VIT. C	CALCIUM	IRON	F.ACID	FIBRE
gm	kcal	gm	gm	gm	mcg	mg	mg	mg	mcg	gm
196	56	3.5	9.9	0.2	507.1	56.5	54.1	3.1	2.2	1.4

Tomato Salsa

Prep. time :

15 minutes.

No Cooking.

Makes 1½ cups.

This Mexican style tangy tomato dip makes a perfect accompaniment for Baked Tortilla Chips, page 92. Believe me, the delicious flavour of vegetables perked with oregano does not fail to please. This treat provides vitamins A and C and fibre from low calorie veggies like tomato, capsicum and coriander.

1 cup tomatoes, deseeded and finely chopped
1 spring onion, finely chopped
1 tablespoon finely chopped capsicum
2 tablespoons finely chopped coriander
1 green chilli, finely chopped
½ teaspoon cumin (jeera) powder
¼ teaspoon oregano
salt to taste

1 Combine all the ingredients together and refrigerate for at least 3 to 4 hours.
2 Mash the salsa slightly to make it like a sauce.
  Serve with the baked tortilla chips.

≈ Nutritive values for 1½ cups : ≈

AMT	ENERGY	PROTEIN	CHO	FAT	VIT. A	VIT. C	CALCIUM	IRON	F.ACID	FIBRE
gm	kcal	gm	gm	gm	mcg	mg	mg	mg	mcg	gm
217	56	2.2	10.9	0.5	1018.6	70.7	110.5	1.5	49.0	1.7

Hakka Mushrooms

Picture on page 58

Prep. time :

10 minutes.

Cooking time :

15 minutes.

Serves 2.

A mushroom lover's delight! Tossed with garlic and soya sauce, these mushrooms are sure to tickle anyone's taste buds. Loaded with iron and fibre and low in carbohydrates, this hearty and healthy dish will make a full meal, if the mushrooms are tossed with ½ cup of boiled noodles.

2 cups mushrooms, cut into halves
4 cloves garlic, finely chopped
1 green chilli, finely chopped
2½ tablespoons soya sauce
1 teaspoon cornflour
1 cup spring onion greens, finely chopped
a pinch chilli powder
1 teaspoon oil
salt to taste

1. Dissolve the cornflour in 2 tablespoons of water and the soya sauce and keep aside.
2. Heat the oil in a non-stick pan, add the garlic and green chilli and sauté for 2 minutes.
3. Add the mushrooms and salt and sauté for 3 to 4 minutes.
4. Add the cornflour mixture and sauté for 2 to 3 minutes till the sauce coats the mushrooms.
5. Add the spring onion greens and mix well.
6. Sprinkle the chilli powder and serve immediately.

❧ Nutritive values per serving : ❧

AMT	ENERGY	PROTEIN	CHO	FAT	VIT. A	VIT. C	CALCIUM	IRON	F.ACID	FIBRE
gm	kcal	gm	gm	gm	mcg	mg	mg	mg	mcg	gm
55	31	1.6	3.8	1.4	59.7	8.5	13.5	1.0	11.2	0.8

Exchange list per serving :

CEREAL	PULSE	VEGETABLE	FRUIT	MILK	FAT
–	–	¾	–	–	¼

Spicy Stir Fried Baby Corn

Picture on page 58

Prep. time :

10 minutes.

Cooking time :

10 minutes.

Serves 4.

Stir frying is a very popular method of cooking food that originated in China. It is a nutritious and convenient way of cooking as it makes use of minimal oil. The short cooking time makes the vegetables more succulent and preserves their texture and natural flavours while preventing the loss of water soluble vitamins like B and C.

I've used baby corn in the dish, as this versatile vegetable is extremely low in carbohydrates. Instead of the baby corn, you can even use mushrooms or Low Fat Paneer, page 154.

200 grams (2 packets) baby corn, sliced into 2 lengthwise
1 green chilli, finely chopped
1½ teaspoons ginger, finely chopped
1½ teaspoon garlic, finely chopped
1 teaspoon soya sauce
2 teaspoons tomato-chilli sauce
1 teaspoon cornflour
a few slices of red and green capsicum
1 teaspoon oil
salt and pepper to taste

1 Combine the soya sauce, tomato-chilli sauce and cornflour with 2 tablespoons of water in a bowl. Keep aside.
2 Heat the oil in non-stick pan, add the baby corn and sauté over a high flame for 4 to 5 minutes.
3 Add the green chilli, ginger and garlic and sauté for another 2 minutes.
4 Add the cornflour and sauce mixture. Mix well over a high flame till the sauce coats the baby corn evenly.
5 Toss in the capsicum, add salt and pepper and mix well. Serve hot.

❧ Nutritive values per serving : ❧

AMT	ENERGY	PROTEIN	CHO	FAT	VIT. A	VIT. C	CALCIUM	IRON	F.ACID	FIBRE
gm	kcal	gm	gm	gm	mcg	mg	mg	mg	mcg	gm
66	84	2.3	15.0	2.6	73.5	13.1	3.4	0.3	13.3	1.5

Exchange list per serving :

CEREAL	PULSE	VEGETABLE	FRUIT	MILK	FAT
¼	—	2	—	—	¼

Eggplant Dip

Prep. time :

10 minutes.

Cooking time :

30 minutes.

Makes 1½ cups

(15 servings).

The Middle Eastern name for this dip is Baba Ganoush which is eaten with whole wheat pita breads (page 123) as an appetiser or a snack. While it may not sound very appetising to have a brinjal dip…, trust me you will not even realize that you are eating brinjal. Brinjals are a rich source of iron which is an important component of our blood.

Today a variety of readymade dips are available in the market. But it is wiser to make one at home since it will be free of preservatives as well as more nutritious. You can even use it as a sandwich spread as it is healthier as compared to a calorie laden cheese or mayonnaise based sandwich.

1 large (250 grams) brinjal (baingan / eggplant)
2 large cloves garlic
¼ cup thick low fat curds, page 153
1 green chilli, chopped
¼ teaspoon cumin (jeera) powder
2 spring onions, finely chopped
1 tablespoon chopped coriander
salt to taste

1 Prick the brinjal with a fork and place over a grill or gas flame. Rotate it regularly till the peel is almost burnt and the flesh is soft and pulpy.
2 Allow it to cool. Carefully peel the burnt portion of the skin and discard it.
3 Put the brinjal pulp in a blender, add the garlic, curds and green chilli and blend till it is a smooth purée.
4 Transfer to a bowl, add the cumin powder, spring onions, coriander and salt and mix well.
5 Chill thoroughly and serve with whole wheat pita bread or vegetable crudits.

❧ Nutritive values for 1½ cups : ❧

AMT	ENERGY	PROTEIN	CHO	FAT	VIT. A	VIT. C	CALCIUM	IRON	F.ACID	FIBRE
gm	kcal	gm	gm	gm	mcg	mg	mg	mg	mcg	gm
332	116	6.4	21.0	0.8	392.5	42.4	153.7	1.5	89.4	3.7

❧ Hummus ❧

Prep. time :

20 minutes.

Cooking time :

15 minutes.

Makes 1 cup.

Chick peas are one of the most versatile beans that abound in all major nutrients like vitamin A, vitamin C, iron, calcium as well as fibre. This is a healthier version of the traditional hummus that is made using loads of olive oil. Serve this lemony-garlic chick pea spread on thin whole wheat pita bread, page 123, and sprinkle a little chilli powder on top for that added spice.

I often serve leftover hummus with whole wheat toast for breakfast as a healthier substitute for butter. Try it and I am sure you will enjoy it.

½ cup chick peas (kabuli chana)
2 cloves garlic
juice of 1 lemon
4 tablespoons low fat curds, page 153
salt to taste
1 teaspoon olive oil

For the garnish
1 teaspoon chopped parsley
chilli powder

1   Soak the chick peas in water for 6 hours making sure that they are covered with water.
2   Cook the chick peas in a pressure cooker. Cool and drain. Keep the drained liquid aside.

3   Put the oil, lemon juice, curds, cooked chick peas, garlic, salt and some of the strained water in a blender and blend until smooth. If the mixture is too thick, add 2 to 3 tablespoons of water.
4   Place this mixture in a serving plate and sprinkle parsley and chilli powder on top.
Serve with thin strips of vegetables or with whole wheat pita bread.

❧ Nutritive values per cup : ❧

AMT	ENERGY	PROTEIN	CHO	FAT	VIT. A	VIT. C	CALCIUM	IRON	F.ACID	FIBRE
gm	kcal	gm	gm	gm	mcg	mg	mg	mg	mcg	gm
86	232	9.7	31.6	7.5	159.9	16.8	191.2	2.3	83.6	2.3

Celery Garlic Toasts

Prep. time :

5 minutes.

Cooking time :

15 minutes.

Makes 4 toasts.

Baking time :

15 minutes.

Baking temperature :

180°C (360°F).

A delicious starter made with celery and garlic ground together to make an aromatic spread in place of butter.

Both celery and garlic are beneficial for diabetics. I have chosen celery for this recipe as it is very low in carbohydrates and is a storehouse of vitamin A, vitamin C and iron (which is required for healthy eyes, immunity and blood). Garlic on the other hand is helpful in preventing heart disease by reducing the occurrence of clot formation in blood (that can block the arteries).

Serve it with your favourite soup or whole wheat pasta to make a wholesome meal. I assure you that you will not miss the BUTTER.

4 slices of whole wheat bread

To be coarsely ground into a paste
¼ cup celery, chopped
2 to 3 cloves garlic
salt to taste

1   Apply the ground celery paste equally on all 4 toasts.
2   Bake in a pre-heated oven at 180°C (360°F) for 10 minutes or till the toasts are evenly browned.
3   Cut into halves and serve immediately.

AMT	ENERGY	PROTEIN	CHO	FAT	VIT. A	VIT. C	CALCIUM	IRON	F.ACID	FIBRE
gm	kcal	gm	gm	gm	mcg	mg	mg	mg	mcg	gm
26	50	1.8	10.0	0.3	31.2	0.4	17.4	0.7	0.0	0.3

Exchange list per toast :

CEREAL	PULSE	VEGETABLE	FRUIT	MILK	FAT		CEREAL	PULSE	VEGETABLE	FRUIT	MILK	FAT
¼	—	1	—	—	—	OR	½	—	—	—	—	—

Whole Wheat Corn Flake Rolls

Prep. time :

30 minutes.

Cooking time :

20 minutes.

Makes 4 rolls.

Baking temperature :

200°C (400°F).

Extremely simple and nourishing — all the three ingredients i.e. corn flakes, whole wheat flour and wheat bran used in these rolls are rich in fibre and corn flakes also contribute to its iron content. Soft yet crunchy, these delightful rolls are best if served warm as an accompaniment to your favourite salad or soup.

I've used 1 teaspoon of sugar in this recipe, as it is required for the yeast to ferment which is not possible with the use of sugar substitute.

¼ cup corn flakes
1 cup whole wheat flour (gehun ka atta)
2 tablespoons wheat bran
1 teaspoon sugar
1 teaspoon olive oil
¾ teaspoon salt
1 teaspoon (5 grams) fresh yeast

Dieter's Pizza, *page 137.*

1. Combine all the ingredients except the corn flakes and knead into a soft dough using water.
2. Knead the dough till it is smooth and elastic.
3. Cover with a damp muslin and keep aside (to prove) approx. 20 to 30 minutes till it doubles in volume. Press tightly to release the air.
4. Add the corn flakes to the "proved" dough and knead again till it is well mixed.
5. Divide the dough into four equal parts and roll out each portion in the shaped dinner rolls. Place on a lightly greased baking tray.
6. Cover with a muslin cloth and allow to "prove" once more till the rolls double in volume.
7. Bake in a pre-heated oven at 200°C (400°F) for 15 to 20 minutes. Serve hot.

❧ Nutritive values per roll : ❧

AMT	ENERGY	PROTEIN	CHO	FAT	VIT. A	VIT. C	CALCIUM	IRON	F.ACID	FIBRE
gm	kcal	gm	gm	gm	mcg	mg	mg	mg	mcg	gm
37	131	4.4	23.8	2.0	19.1	0.0	20.3	2.3	25.1	1.1

Exchange list per roll :

CEREAL	PULSE	VEGETABLE	FRUIT	MILK	FAT
1	–	–	–	–	¼

Malai Peda, page 144.

SOUPS

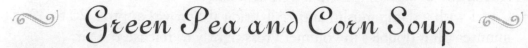

Green Pea and Corn Soup

Prep. time :
15 minutes.

Cooking time :
15 minutes.

Serves 4.

Corn is the staple cereal used in Mexican cuisine. Green peas are used to thicken this soup and to add a substantial amount of fibre too. Coriander and garlic lend delicate aromatic flavours that complement the corn and peas making this soup difficult to resist.

This delicious broth makes a wholesome and heart-warming meal if served with whole wheat bread.

2 cups fresh green peas
1 cup sweet corn kernels
½ onion, chopped
1 clove garlic, crushed
salt to taste

For serving
¼ cup low fat milk, page 152
1 teaspoon chopped coriander
1 teaspoon chopped mint

1 Combine the peas, corn, onion, garlic, salt and 4 cups of water and simmer for 10 minutes or until tender. Cool and blend in a mixer to get a smooth purée.
2 Just before serving, add the milk, coriander, mint and salt and bring to a boil. Serve hot.

❧ Nutritive values per serving : ❧

AMT	ENERGY	PROTEIN	CHO	FAT	VIT. A	VIT. C	CALCIUM	IRON	F.ACID	FIBRE
gm	kcal	gm	gm	gm	mcg	mg	mg	mg	mcg	gm
118	109	6.8	21.3	0.1	89.1	9.6	41.2	1.4	15.5	3.7

Exchange list per serving :

CEREAL	PULSE	VEGETABLE	FRUIT	MILK	FAT
—	—	2½	—	½	¼

Mein Chow Soup

Prep. time :

15 minutes.

Cooking time :

10 minutes.

Serves 6.

The abundance of intensely flavoured fresh vegetables makes this soup rich, tasty and extremely satisfying without the use of too much oil. Oats have been added to thicken the soup as well as to add fibre to your diet.

I find this soup an excellent remedy for a cold .... a hot bowlful usually chases away congestion that accompanies a cold and rejuvenates my spirits too.

1 tablespoon finely chopped fresh mint leaves
1 tablespoon chopped coriander
2 teaspoons chopped garlic
2 teaspoons grated ginger
2 tablespoons finely chopped tomato
2 tablespoons finely chopped capsicum
2 tablespoons finely chopped cauliflower
2 tablespoons finely chopped carrot
2 tablespoons finely chopped cabbage
1 tablespoon quick cooking oats
½ teaspoon pepper powder
1 green chilli, finely chopped (optional)
1 teaspoon oil
salt to taste

For the topping
2 tablespoons chopped coriander

1   Heat the oil in a wok on a high flame.
2   Add the mint leaves, coriander, garlic, ginger, vegetables and salt and stir fry for 2 to 3 minutes over a high flame.
3   Add 4 cups of hot water, the oats, salt and pepper powder and bring to a boil. Serve hot, garnished with the coriander.

Nutritive values per serving :

AMT	ENERGY	PROTEIN	CHO	FAT	VIT. A	VIT. C	CALCIUM	IRON	F.ACID	FIBRE
gm	kcal	gm	gm	gm	mcg	mg	mg	mg	mcg	gm
23	18	0.5	1.7	1.0	204.7	17.9	11.3	0.3	3.4	0.3

Exchange list per serving :

CEREAL	PULSE	VEGETABLE	FRUIT	MILK	FAT
–	–	½	–	–	⅛

Tum Yum Soup

A flavourful soup that is truly refreshing as the chillies, lemon grass and other ingredients unite to create a harmonious bouquet of flavours. Enjoy the freshness of succulent mushrooms and cauliflower that are simmered in this delightful stock which is irresistible.

Prep. time :

15 minutes.

Cooking time :

10 minutes.

Serves 6.

5 cups clear vegetable stock, page 155
1 green chilli, cut lengthwise
10 fresh mushrooms, sliced
10 to 12 cauliflower florets, parboiled
1 tablespoon roughly chopped lemon grass
1 teaspoon lemon juice
salt to taste

To serve
chillies in vinegar

1. Put the stock to boil.
2. Add the green chilli, mushrooms, cauliflower, lemon grass and salt and boil for 2 to 3 minutes.
3. Add the lemon juice.
   Serve hot, with chillies in vinegar.

Handy tip : You can also add other vegetables like broccoli and baby corn instead of the mushrooms.

AMT	ENERGY	PROTEIN	CHO	FAT	VIT. A	VIT. C	CALCIUM	IRON	F.ACID	FIBRE
gm	kcal	gm	gm	gm	mcg	mg	mg	mg	mcg	gm
25	34	1.1	7.2	0.2	984.0	12.7	48.4	1.2	12.7	1.1

Exchange list per serving :

CEREAL	PULSE	VEGETABLE	FRUIT	MILK	FAT
–	–	1½	–	–	–

≈ Nourishing Barley Soup ≈

Picture on page 75

Barley is a cereal that is not usually used in everyday cooking. It is however a great source of protein, iron and fibre and tastes good too, if cooked with flavourful ingredients as I have done in this broth.

The combination of masoor dal along with barley i.e. a pulse with a cereal makes this soup a complete source of protein, which is otherwise lacking in a vegetarian diet. The vegetables add plenty of colour and fibre to this nourishing broth. Add freshly ground pepper towards the end to perk up this soup.

Prep. time :

10 minutes.

Cooking time :

20 minutes.

Serves 4.

2 tablespoons pearl barley, soaked for 3 to 4 hours
2 tablespoons whole masoor (whole red lentils),
soaked overnight and drained
1 large clove garlic, chopped
3 spring onions (white and greens separated), finely
chopped
¼ cup carrots, diced
½ tomato, chopped
2 tablespoons chopped coriander
1 teaspoon oil
salt and freshly ground pepper to taste

1. Drain the soaked barley and keep aside.
2. Heat the oil in a pressure cooker, add the garlic and spring onion whites and sauté till the onion whites turn translucent.
3. Add the barley, masoor, carrots, salt and 4½ cups of water and pressure cook for 3 to 4 whistles. Cool slightly.
4. Add the spring onion greens, tomato, coriander and pepper and bring to a boil.

Serve hot.

Handy tip : Pearl barley is easily available at most grocery stores and also at chemist shops.

❧ Nutritive values per serving : ❧

AMT	ENERGY	PROTEIN	CHO	FAT	VIT. A	VIT. C	CALCIUM	IRON	F.ACID	FIBRE
gm	kcal	gm	gm	gm	mcg	mg	mg	mg	mcg	gm
34	51	2.0	7.8	1.4	251.5	8.5	19.5	0.7	6.0	0.6

Exchange list per serving :

CEREAL	PULSE	VEGETABLE	FRUIT	MILK	FAT
¼	—	½	—	—	¼

Lentil and Vegetable Broth

Prep. time :

20 minutes.

Cooking time :

20 minutes.

Serves 6.

A thick and creamy soup that's satiating and will also pamper your taste buds. The dal, tomatoes and onion based stock lends a creamy texture and the sautéed vegetables add that necessary crunch. Feel free to choose any fresh vegetables of your choice if cabbage or spinach are not your favourites.
Serve hot with Celery Garlic Toasts, page 99.

For the stock
2 tablespoons yellow moong dal (split yellow gram), washed
2 onions
2 large tomatoes

For the topping
1 onion, chopped
1/3 cup cabbage, shredded
1/3 cup spinach (palak), chopped
2 tablespoons baked beans or tomato ketchup
1 tomato, finely chopped
1½ teaspoons oil
salt and pepper to taste

For the stock
1 Cut the onions and tomatoes into big pieces.
2 Add the moong dal and 4½ cups of water and cook in a pressure cooker.
3 When cool, blend in a liquidiser and keep aside.

How to proceed
1 Heat the oil and sauté the onion for 1 minute.
2 Add the cabbage and spinach and sauté again for 1 minute.
3 Add the stock and simmer for 10 minutes.
4 Add the beans, tomato, salt and pepper and bring to a boil.
Serve hot, with celery garlic toasts.

AMT	ENERGY	PROTEIN	CHO	FAT	VIT. A	VIT. C	CALCIUM	IRON	F.ACID	FIBRE
gm	kcal	gm	gm	gm	mcg	mg	mg	mg	mcg	gm
94	62	2.1	10.2	1.5	382.3	22.2	46.3	0.8	26.6	0.7

Exchange list per serving :

CEREAL	PULSE	VEGETABLE	FRUIT	MILK	FAT
–	¼	1	–	–	¼

❧ Sweet Corn and Spring Onion Soup ❧

Prep. time :

10 minutes.

Cooking time :

15 minutes.

Serves 4.

A rich and creamy soup made with a combination of sweet corn and spring onions enhanced by a touch of garlic and pepper. Low in calories and carbohydrates, this soup is especially good in the monsoon when corn is abundantly available.

2 spring onions, chopped (whites and greens separated)
1 cup sweet corn kernels
2 cloves garlic, chopped
1 teaspoon oil
salt and pepper to taste

1   Combine the sweet corn with 1 cup of water and blend into a purée.
2   Heat the oil in a non-stick pan, add the spring onion whites and sauté for 2 or 3 minutes.
3   Add the garlic and the puréed corn and sauté for 5 to 7 minutes till the corn purée is cooked.
4   Add 2½ cups of water and bring to a boil.
5   Add the spring onion greens and simmer for 2 to 3 minutes.
6   Season with salt and pepper and serve hot.

❧ Nutritive values per serving : ❧

AMT	ENERGY	PROTEIN	CHO	FAT	VIT. A	VIT. C	CALCIUM	IRON	F.ACID	FIBRE
gm	kcal	gm	gm	gm	mcg	mg	mg	mg	mcg	gm
49	52	1.7	8.2	1.5	77.5	10.3	14.0	0.7	2.6	1.0

Exchange list per serving :

CEREAL	PULSE	VEGETABLE	FRUIT	MILK	FAT
—	—	1½	—	—	¼

Burnt Corn Salad

Prep. time :
10 minutes.

Cooking time :
10 minutes.

Serves 4.

Mexicans love a smoked or barbecued flavour in their food. This corn salad is a good example of that. Fresh corn kernels are grilled over an open flame to impart a burnt-smoked flavour to this salad. Extremely low in calories and fat and high in fibre, this is a perfect choice for diabetics who have high post lunch blood sugar levels.

Tomatoes, onions and capsicum blend extremely well with corn and add vitamins like A and C. The olive oil and lemon juice dressing adds a tangy flavour and vitamin C that helps to strengthens our immunity.

2 large sweet corn cobs
1 white onion, sliced
1 capsicum, sliced
1 tomato, sliced
salt to taste

To be mixed into a dressing
1 teaspoon olive oil
2 teaspoons lemon juice
2 pinches chilli powder

1 Roast the corn cob over an open flame until the corn is slightly burnt.
2 Using a sharp knife, remove the corn kernels from the cob. Keep aside.
3 Combine the corn kernels, onion, capsicum, tomato and salt.
4 Pour the dressing on top and toss well.
   Serve immediately.

Nutritive values per serving :

AMT	ENERGY	PROTEIN	CHO	FAT	VIT. A	VIT. C	CALCIUM	IRON	F.ACID	FIBRE
gm	kcal	gm	gm	gm	mcg	mg	mg	mg	mcg	gm
127	102	3.3	21.5	1.5	237.8	57.0	22.7	0.7	24.0	2.4

CEREAL	PULSE	VEGETABLE	FRUIT	MILK	FAT
—	—	3	—	—	¼

❧ Exotic Salad ❧

Prep. time :

10 minutes.

No Cooking.

Serves 4.

Earthy broccoli florets, iceberg lettuce and crispy celery stalks in combination with bean sprouts provide a wonderful array of flavours to delight the palate and also provide a wealth of nutrients.

The puréed melon adds volume to the dressing making it creamier and of a coating consistency to flavour the vegetables and sprouts. Feel free to use any combination of vegetables that are handy.

1½ cups iceberg lettuce, torn into pieces
½ cup bean sprouts
½ cup broccoli florets, blanched
2 celery stalks, chopped

For the dressing
1 cup ripe muskmelon (kharbooja), chopped
½ teaspoon roasted cumin seeds (jeera), crushed
3 tablespoons chopped coriander
salt and pepper to taste

For the dressing

1. Blend the muskmelon to a smooth purée in a blender.
2. Add the remaining ingredients and mix well. Refrigerate till required.

How to proceed

1. Combine all the ingredients for the salad in a bowl and refrigerate.
2. Just before serving, add the dressing and toss well.
   Serve immediately.

Handy tip : Add ½ sachet of sugar substitute to the dressing if the melon is not sweet enough.

❧ Nutritive values per serving : ❧

AMT	ENERGY	PROTEIN	CHO	FAT	VIT. A	VIT. C	CALCIUM	IRON	F.ACID	FIBRE
gm	kcal	gm	gm	gm	mcg	mg	mg	mg	mcg	gm
118	51	3.8	8.3	0.4	999.4	24.8	69.6	2.6	3.6	1.0

Exchange list per serving :

CEREAL	PULSE	VEGETABLE	FRUIT	MILK	FAT
–	–	1	½	–	–

❧ Cucumber Salad ❧

Prep. time :

15 minutes.

No Cooking.

Serves 4.

Cucumber is a vegetable with a high water content and is therefore relatively low in calories and carbohydrates. Try having cucumber with its peel on which itself is a great source of fibre and many more nutrients. The fat free lemon juice and soya sauce dressing enhances this salad, especially when it is served chilled.

1 cup cucumber, peeled and diced
1 cup tomatoes, deseeded and cubed
1 cup spring onions, sliced

To be mixed into a dressing
½ green chilli, finely chopped
1 clove garlic, finely chopped
1 teaspoon soya sauce
a pinch sugar substitute
juice of ½ lemon
salt to taste

Combine all the ingredients in a bowl and toss the salad. Serve immediately.

Handy tip : You can make large quantities of this dressing and refrigerate it till required. I often blend all the ingredients in a blender or grind them in a "silbatta" so that all the ingredients marry well.

❧ Nutritive values per serving : ❧

AMT	ENERGY	PROTEIN	CHO	FAT	VIT. A	VIT. C	CALCIUM	IRON	F.ACID	FIBRE
gm	kcal	gm	gm	gm	mcg	mg	mg	mg	mcg	gm
89	21	0.7	4.3	0.2	136.9	15.8	31.5	0.5	17.2	0.6

Exchange list per serving :

CEREAL	PULSE	VEGETABLE	FRUIT	MILK	FAT
–	–	1	–	–	–

ᔆ· Oriental Salad ·ᔆ

Prep. time :

10 minutes.

Cooking time :

2 minutes.

Serves 4.

Colourful vegetables are dressed in a delicious garlic and basil flavoured dressing. The lemon and basil dressing in this salad serves as an excellent source of vitamin C which further aids in the absorption of iron from our diet.

If you cannot find fresh basil, substitute it with ¼ teaspoon of dried basil, as dried herbs are more potent than fresh herbs.

½ cup spring onions, diced
½ cup fresh mushrooms, sliced
½ cup baby corn, diced and blanched
¾ cup bean sprouts
½ cup red and green capsicums, cubed
½ cup cucumber, diced

For the dressing
1 teaspoon olive oil
3 cloves garlic, finely chopped

115

1 tablespoon fresh basil leaves, finely chopped
2 teaspoons lemon juice
1 sachet sugar substitute
salt and pepper to taste

For the dressing

1 Heat the oil in a non-stick pan, add the garlic and sauté till it browns lightly.
2 Add the basil leaves and mix well. Cool completely.
3 Add the lemon juice, sugar substitute, salt and pepper and mix well.

How to proceed

1 Combine all the ingredients in a bowl and toss lightly. Refrigerate.
2 Just before serving, add the dressing to the salad and toss well. Serve immediately.

❧ Nutritive values per serving : ❧

AMT	ENERGY	PROTEIN	CHO	FAT	VIT. A	VIT. C	CALCIUM	IRON	F.ACID	FIBRE
gm	kcal	gm	gm	gm	mcg	mg	mg	mg	mcg	gm
82	94	4.9	14.9	1.7	95.3	25.8	30.4	1.2	4.4	1.3

Exchange list per serving :

CEREAL	PULSE	VEGETABLE	FRUIT	MILK	FAT
—	½	1½	—	—	¼

~ Orange Tabbouleh ~

Prep. time :

15 minutes.

Cooking time :

10 minutes.

Serves 4.

Bulgur (which is often referred to as broken wheat or dalia) is the healthiest form of wheat available. The most important nutrient retained by this cereal form is fibre that makes it a low glycemic index food and thus helps to prevent a quick rise in blood sugar levels.

In contrast, wheat products like rava, maida and pasta lose many of their nutrients as a result of processing and refining. You can also make nourishing dishes like khichdi and pulao using bulgur wheat. I have even included a delicious Spicy Vegetable Risotto, page 140, which makes use of bulgur wheat.

Packed with protein, calcium, vitamin C, vitamin A, iron and fibre, this salad is spiked up with a lot of Mediterranean flavours like olive oil, oranges, parsley, lemon juice and spring onions which will not fail to tingle your taste buds. Allow the salad to rest for a while after you toss it so that all the flavours mellow and blend into harmonious flavours.

1 cup broken wheat (dalia)
1 tablespoon grated orange zest
2 spring onions (including greens), finely chopped
1 tomato, diced
½ cup parsley, finely chopped
1 teaspoon lemon juice
2 teaspoons olive oil
¼ teaspoon sugar substitute
1½ cups orange segments
salt to taste

1 Cook the broken wheat in 1½ cups of water for 10 minutes till it is tender.
2 Drain and pour cold water over the broken wheat to cool. Drain again and keep aside.
3 Combine all the ingredients in a bowl and mix well.
4 Refrigerate for at least 1 hour before serving so that all the flavours blend.

Handy tips :

1 While grating the orange zest, do not grate the white pith as it is bitter and will impart its flavour to the salad.
2 Select sweet oranges as their natural sweetness will enhance the flavour of this salad.

❧ Nutritive values per serving : ❦

AMT	ENERGY	PROTEIN	CHO	FAT	VIT. A	VIT. C	CALCIUM	IRON	F.ACID	FIBRE
gm	kcal	gm	gm	gm	mcg	mg	mg	mg	mcg	gm
150	202	4.0	39.0	3.3	852.3	31.2	55.2	2.5	13.4	1.3

Exchange list per serving :

CEREAL	PULSE	VEGETABLE	FRUIT	MILK	FAT
1	–	1	1¼	–	½

❦ Spring Salad ❦

Prep. time :

10 minutes.

No Cooking.

Serves 4.

A colourful salad that's sure to appeal to your taste buds as well your eyes. This fibre rich salad will also add plenty of vitamin A, vitamin C, calcium and iron. Since vitamin C is a very volatile nutrient, it should be added just before serving, so do use freshly squeezed lemon juice. You can also add a dash of finely chopped garlic to this dressing if you like.

Wash the spinach and lettuce in ice cold water to keep them crisp. Then dry them by placing them on a dry towel, so that they absorb the dressing well.

For the salad
1 cup spinach (palak) leaves, washed and torn
2 cups lettuce, washed and torn
2 large oranges, peeled and segmented
1 cup bean sprouts
2 spring onions, chopped

To be mixed into a dressing
1 tablespoon lemon juice
1 teaspoon olive oil
salt and pepper to taste

1 Combine all the salad ingredients in a bowl and refrigerate.
2 Just before serving, add the dressing and toss well.
  Serve immediately.

❧ Nutritive values per serving : ❧

AMT	ENERGY	PROTEIN	CHO	FAT	VIT. A	VIT. C	CALCIUM	IRON	F.ACID	FIBRE
gm	kcal	gm	gm	gm	mcg	mg	mg	mg	mcg	gm
191	117	5.9	18.8	2.0	2349 7	33.6	96.9	3.0	22.0	1.5

Exchange list per serving :

CEREAL	PULSE	VEGETABLE	FRUIT	MILK	FAT
—	½	1	½	—	¼

Tangy Italian Salad

Prep. time :

10 minutes.

No Cooking.

Serves 4.

Firm ripe tomatoes are combined with cool cucumbers and crisp lettuce leaves tossed in low fat basil flavoured vinaigrette.
Tomatoes provide vitamin A and fibre while lettuce and cucumbers contribute fibre as well as vitamin C and iron.

For the salad
2 cups tomatoes (quartered and deseeded)
1 cup cucumber, sliced
2 cups lettuce leaves, torn into pieces

To be mixed into a dressing
1 teaspoon crushed garlic
1 teaspoon fresh basil leaves, chopped
1½ tablespoons lemon juice
1 teaspoon olive oil
salt and pepper to taste

1   Combine all the ingredients in a salad bowl and chill thoroughly.
2   Just before serving, add the dressing and toss well.
    Serve immediately.

❧ Nutritive values per serving : ❧

AMT	ENERGY	PROTEIN	CHO	FAT	VIT. A	VIT. C	CALCIUM	IRON	F.ACID	FIBRE
gm	kcal	gm	gm	gm	mcg	mg	mg	mg	mcg	gm
200	54	2.6	6.8	1.8	1077.0	35.5	88.2	2.6	27.7	1.3

Exchange list per serving :

CEREAL	PULSE	VEGETABLE	FRUIT	MILK	FAT
—	—	1½	—	—	¼

Lemony Yoghurt Salad

Prep. time :

10 minutes.

No Cooking.

Serves 4.

Packed with protein, vitamin A, vitamin C, calcium, iron and fibre, this salad is extremely healthy, nourishing and tasty. This refreshing salad is full of the goodness of apples, lettuce, celery and corn flakes and is served in a creamy and tangy basil flavoured dressing that is sweetened with grated apple.

Apply a little lemon juice to the apples before refrigerating to avoid discolouration due to exposure to air.

For the salad
2 cups apple, cubed
4 tablespoons celery, finely chopped
4 cups lettuce leaves, torn into pieces
½ cup corn flakes

To be mixed into a dressing
¼ cup fresh low fat curds, page 153
zest of 1 lemon
1 tablespoon finely chopped basil
2 tablespoons grated apple
salt and pepper to taste

1   Combine all the ingredients for the salad, except the corn flakes and mix well.
2   Chill for at least 2 hours.
3   Add the corn flakes and the dressing to the salad just before serving. Toss the salad and serve immediately.

❧ Nutritive values per serving : ❧

AMT	ENERGY	PROTEIN	CHO	FAT	VIT. A	VIT. C	CALCIUM	IRON	F.ACID	FIBRE
gm	kcal	gm	gm	gm	mcg	mg	mg	mg	mcg	gm
237	88	4.3	15.9	0.8	1646.5	17.4	131.0	4.9	0.2	1.6

Exchange list per per serving :

CEREAL	PULSE	VEGETABLE	FRUIT	MILK	FAT		CEREAL	PULSE	VEGETABLE	FRUIT	MILK	FAT
½	–	½	½	–	–	OR	½	–	–	1	–	–

MAIN COURSES

~ Burritos ~

Prep. time :

10 minutes.

Cooking time :

10 minutes.

Makes 6 burritos.

Burritos are warm, soft flour tortillas filled with savoury ingredients like refried beans, tomatoes, onions and salsa. I've substituted the cheese used in this traditional recipe with low fat paneer to prevent a rise in blood cholesterol levels. Assemble the burrito just before eating and serve immediately, topped with Green Tomato Salsa, page 93, to relish the real Mexican flavours.

6 corn tortillas, page 156

For the filling
1 recipe refried beans, page 157
½ cup cabbage, shredded
½ cup spring onions, finely chopped
½ cup low fat paneer, page 154, grated

For serving
1 recipe green tomato salsa, page 93 or tomato salsa, page 94

1 Place a portion of the refried beans, cabbage, spring onion and paneer on one end of a corn tortilla.
2 Roll up the tortilla, starting from the end where the filling is placed.
3 Repeat with the remaining tortillas and filling.
4 Cook the burritos lightly on a non-stick pan.
5 Serve each burrito with 1 teaspoon of green tomato salsa or tomato salsa.

~ Nutritive values per burrito : ~

AMT	ENERGY	PROTEIN	CHO	FAT	VIT. A	VIT. C	CALCIUM	IRON	F.ACID	FIBRE
gm	kcal	gm	gm	gm	mcg	mg	mg	mg	mcg	gm
31	104	5.1	15.3	2.4	138.9	17.1	135.7	1.0	11.2	0.8

CEREAL	PULSE	VEGETABLE	FRUIT	MILK	FAT
—	½	2	—	¼	¼

❧ Mexican Pita Pockets ❧

Picture on page 127

Soft pita breads made with whole wheat flour and filled with a spicy Mexican bean filling will help to keep the blood sugar levels in check. Served with salad and a delicious mint dressing which add a bouquet of tantalising flavours to this dish.

Prep. time :

15 minutes.

Cooking time :

30 minutes.

Makes 4 pita pockets.

For the whole wheat pita breads
¾ cup whole wheat flour (gehun ka atta)
¾ teaspoon fresh yeast, crumbled
½ teaspoon salt

For the mexican bean patties
½ cup kidney beans (rajma), soaked overnight
2 cloves garlic, finely chopped
1 spring onion (whites and greens separated), finely chopped
½ tomato, chopped
¼ cup capsicum, finely chopped
1 teaspoon chilli powder
1 teaspoon roasted cumin (jeera) powder
1 teaspoon oil
salt to taste

To be blended into a mint dressing
1 cup low fat curds, page 153
¼ cup chopped mint leaves
½ green chilli
½ teaspoon roasted cumin seeds (jeera)
salt to taste

Other ingredients
2 tomatoes, finely chopped
1 cup lettuce, shredded

For the whole wheat pita breads
1 Combine all the ingredients in a bowl and knead into a soft dough using enough water. Knead until it is smooth and elastic.
2 Cover the dough with a wet muslin cloth and allow it to prove till it doubles in volume (approx. 15 to 20 minutes).
3 Press the dough lightly to remove the air.
4 Divide the dough into 2 equal parts. Roll out each portion into a circle of 100 mm. (4") diameter and 6 mm. (¼") thickness.
5 Cook the pita breads on a hot tava (griddle) over medium heat on each side for a minute or until the bread puffs up and a cavity is created in the bread. Remove and keep aside.
6 Cut each pita bread into 2 halves and keep aside.

For the mexican bean patties
1 Pressure cook the beans till they are overcooked.
2 Drain and the grind the beans to a coarse paste in a blender or mash them.
3 Heat the oil in a non-stick pan, add the garlic and spring onion whites and sauté till the onion whites turn translucent.
4 Add the rest of ingredients and sauté till the mixture has dried up. Cool completely.
5 Divide the mixture into 4 equal portions. Shape each portion into a patty.

How to proceed
1 Warm the pita bread halves on a tava (griddle).
2 Fill each pita bread half with some tomatoes and lettuce, one bean patty and a spoonful of the mint dressing on top.
3 Repeat for the remaining pita bread halves and other ingredients to make 3 more pita pockets.
Serve immediately.

AMT	ENERGY	PROTEIN	CHO	FAT	VIT. A	VIT. C	CALCIUM	IRON	F.ACID	FIBRE
gm	kcal	gm	gm	gm	mcg	mg	mg	mg	mcg	gm
72	77	4.0	13.2	1.0	324.9	14.8	76.1	1.6	12.4	0.8

Exchange list per pita picket :

CEREAL	PULSE	VEGETABLE	FRUIT	MILK	FAT
¼	¼	1	—	—	¼

⌁ Chinese Fried Rice ⌁

Prep. time :

15 minutes.

Cooking time :

30 minutes.

Serves 6.

Rice is the cereal that diabetics are advised to avoid. Here's a simple and guilt free way to include rice in your diet…. All you have to do is add plenty of vegetables to the rice dish and use minimal oil. Adding vegetables not only enhances its vitamin value but also contributes plenty of fibre that prevents a rapid rise in blood sugar levels after a meal.

Choosing the right kind of rice is important too. Select an unprocessed variety of rice like kolam or brown rice instead of polished rice which has little or no fibre.

1 cup uncooked rice, washed
¾ cup french beans, finely chopped
¾ cup carrots, finely chopped
¼ cup capsicum, finely chopped
2 sticks celery, finely chopped
2 spring onions (whites and greens separated), finely chopped
½ teaspoon soya sauce
1½ teaspoons oil
salt to taste

To serve
green chillies in vinegar

1 Boil the rice in two cups of water. Each grain of the cooked rice should be separate.
2 Heat the oil in a non-stick pan. Add all the vegetables except the spring onion greens. Sprinkle two tablespoons of water and cook for 4 to 5 minutes.
3 Add the rice, soya sauce, spring onion greens and salt. Mix well and sauté for two minutes.
   Serve hot with chillies in vinegar.

Handy tip : You can also use broken wheat (dalia) instead of rice to make this dish.

❧ Nutritive values per serving : ❧

AMT	ENERGY	PROTEIN	CHO	FAT	VIT. A	VIT. C	CALCIUM	IRON	F.ACID	FIBRE
gm	kcal	gm	gm	gm	mcg	mg	mg	mg	mcg	gm
101	177	3.5	35.8	2.2	288.8	17.6	38.3	0.8	14.5	0.8

Exchange list per serving :

CEREAL	PULSE	VEGETABLE	FRUIT	MILK	FAT
1	–	2	–	–	¼

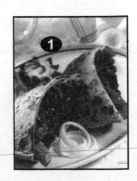

Mexican Pita Pockets, *page 123.*➡

Hot and Sour Vegetables

Prep. time :

20 minutes.

Cooking time :

15 minutes.

Serves 4.

A dish which the entire family will relish.

The freshness of lightly cooked vegetables is enhanced by the aromatic flavours of ginger, garlic, chillies and tomato-chilli sauce. It's a simple and easy way of disguising vegetables and make them lip smackingly delicious, while also adding a wealth of nutrients like vitamin A, vitamin C, calcium and iron.

In addition, this dish is low in calories and carbohydrates and high in fibre which is great for a diabetic diet.

1 cup mixed parboiled vegetables (carrots, broccoli, baby corn and french beans)
¼ cup capsicum, cubed
2 tomatoes, blanched, peeled and grated
1 onion, cubed
1 to 2 chopped green chillies
1½ teaspoons chopped ginger
1½ teaspoons chopped garlic
1 tablespoon celery, chopped
2 teaspoons cornflour
1 teaspoon tomato-chilli sauce
1 teaspoon oil
salt to taste

Diabetic Caramel Custard, *page 148.*

1 Heat the oil in a non-stick pan, add the onion, green chillies, ginger, garlic and celery and sauté for a few minutes.
2 Add the grated tomatoes and salt and simmer it over a medium flame for 4 to 5 minutes, till it thickens.
3 Add all the vegetables and sauté for a few seconds.
4 Combine the cornflour and tomato-chilli sauce with 1 cup of water and add it to the mixture.
5 Bring to a boil and simmer for 4 to 5 minutes till the sauce thickens.
6 Adjust salt to taste and serve hot.

❧ Nutritive values per serving : ❧

AMT	ENERGY	PROTEIN	CHO	FAT	VIT. A	VIT. C	CALCIUM	IRON	F.ACID	FIBRE
gm	kcal	gm	gm	gm	mcg	mg	mg	mg	mcg	gm
86	46	1.3	7.1	1.5	350.5	27.1	41.6	0.7	15.2	0.8

Exchange list per serving :

CEREAL	PULSE	VEGETABLE	FRUIT	MILK	FAT
–	–	1½	–	–	¼

⌒ ⌒ Hakka Noodles ⌒ ⌒

Prep. time :

10 minutes.

Cooking time :

10 minutes.

Serves 2.

A Chinese meal is not complete without noodles, but diabetics are often asked to avoid refined foods like noodles, refined bread and pasta which have a high glycemic index. I have taken the liberty of adding noodles to this menu along with loads of flavourful vegetables and have tossed it in very little oil. The trick is to add lots of fibre by way of vegetables so that the dish looks colourful and also suits the diabetic diet.

Vitamin A, vitamin C, iron, protein and calcium are the nutrients that fortify this recipe.

¾ cup cooked noodles
1 large clove garlic, chopped
½ cup spring onions, chopped (whites and greens separated)
¼ cup carrots, thinly sliced into strips
¼ cup baby corn, thinly sliced into strips
¼ cup capsicum, thinly sliced into strips
½ cup bean sprouts
1 teaspoon soya sauce
1 teaspoon oil
salt to taste

1   Heat the oil in a non-stick pan and add the garlic.
2   Add the spring onion whites, carrots, baby corn, capsicum, bean sprouts and salt and sauté over a high flame for 3 to 4 minutes.
3   Add the noodles, soya sauce and spring onion greens and sauté for another 2 minutes.
    Serve immediately.

⌒ Nutritive values per serving : ⌒

AMT	ENERGY	PROTEIN	CHO	FAT	VIT. A	VIT. C	CALCIUM	IRON	F.ACID	FIBRE
gm	kcal	gm	gm	gm	mcg	mg	mg	mg	mcg	gm
83	116	5.7	17.0	3.0	469.6	29.8	47.9	1.6	5.1	1.7

CEREAL	PULSE	VEGETABLE	FRUIT	MILK	FAT
¼	½	1	–	–	¼

OR

CEREAL	PULSE	VEGETABLE	FRUIT	MILK	FAT
–	¾	1	–	–	¼

Moussaka

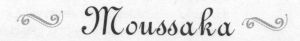

Prep. time :

30 minutes.

Cooking time :

30 minutes.

Serves 4.

Baking time :

20 minutes.

Baking temperature :

200°C (400°F).

Slices of grilled brinjals interlaced with a creamy vegetable mixture and a tangy tomato sauce create a delightful combination of delicate flavours in this classic Greek favourite. To cut down on calories, I have used a low calorie white sauce made with a bottle gourd purée instead of using the usual white sauce.

The brinjal, the vegetable layer and the tomato sauce can be prepared in advance to make a hearty meal in no time by just assembling the ingredients and baking them.

Being baked in an oven, this dish makes use of very little oil and provides oodles of valuable nutrients like vitamin A, vitamin C, calcium and iron along with fibre.

Serve hot.

For the brinjal layer
½ large brinjal (baingan), cut into thin slices (12-15 slices)
1 teaspoon oil
salt to taste

For the vegetable layer
¼ cup baby corn, sliced
¼ cup red capsicum, chopped
¼ cup green capsicum, chopped
1 cup mushrooms, sliced
½ cup bottle gourd (doodhi / lauki), chopped
2 cloves garlic, finely chopped (optional)
1 green chilli, chopped
1 large stalk celery, finely chopped
1 tablespoon whole wheat flour (gehun ka atta)
½ cup low fat milk, page 152
½ teaspoon mixed herbs

1 teaspoon oil
salt to taste

For the tomato sauce
4 large tomatoes
2 bay leaves
4 to 6 peppercorns
1 small onion, chopped
1 teaspoon garlic, chopped
½ capsicum, deseeded
2 tablespoons tomato purée (optional)
½ teaspoon dried oregano
1 teaspoon olive oil or oil
salt to taste

For the brinjal layer

1 Apply a little salt on the brinjal slices and keep aside for 10 minutes.
2 Heat the oil in a non-stick pan and cook the brinjal slices, a few slices at a time, till both sides are golden brown. Keep aside.

For the vegetable layer

1 Boil the bottle gourd in ½ cup of water until soft. Blend in a liquidiser to a smooth purée. (Pressure cooking is also faster).
2 Heat the oil in a non-stick pan, add the garlic, green chilli and celery and sauté for a few seconds.
3 Add the baby corn, red capsicum, green capsicum, mushrooms and wheat flour and sauté for a few minutes.
4 Add the prepared bottle gourd purée, milk, mixed herbs and salt and cook till the mixture is thick. Keep aside.

For the tomato sauce

1 Blanch the tomatoes in boiling water.
2 Peel, cut into quarters and deseed the tomatoes.
3 Chop finely and keep the tomato pulp aside.
4 Heat the olive oil, add the bay leaves and peppercorns and sauté for a few seconds.
5 Add the onion, garlic and capsicum and sauté for a few minutes.

6 Add the tomato pulp (step 3) and allow it to simmer for 10 to 15 minutes until the sauce volume reduces a little.

7 Add the tomato purée and salt and simmer for some more time.

8 Finally, add the oregano and mix well. Remove the capsicum, bay leaves and peppercorns and discard. Use as required.

How to proceed

1 Arrange half the cooked brinjal slices to form a layer on the base of 150 mm. (6") diameter baking dish.

2 Place the vegetable layer over the brinjal slices.

3 Top with another layer of brinjal slices.

4 Cover with the tomato sauce.

5 Bake in a hot oven at 200°C (400°F) for 15 minutes.
Serve hot.

❧ Nutritive values per serving : ❧

AMT	ENERGY	PROTEIN	CHO	FAT	VIT. A	VIT. C	CALCIUM	IRON	F.ACID	FIBRE
gm	kcal	gm	gm	gm	mcg	mg	mg	mg	mcg	gm
181	99	3.4	12.2	4.2	460.6	69.2	93.1	1.4	30.8	1.6

Exchange list per serving :

CEREAL	PULSE	VEGETABLE	FRUIT	MILK	FAT
—	—	—	2	¼	½

~·~ Falafel ~·~

Prep. time :

25 minutes.

Cooking time :

30 minutes.

Makes 12 falafels.

This popular Middle Eastern dish of chick pea patties encased in whole wheat pita bread is spiked up with salad and a low fat curd dressing. Falafel is sold as a quick street side snack as it is filling and also nutritious and also contains plenty of important nutrients like vitamins A and C, iron and fibre.

The high vitamin C content of this dish aids in the absorption of iron that is of utmost importance for the formation of red blood cells.

Serve hot, with a bowl of salad to make a healthy snack or a nourishing brunch.

For the pita bread
1 cup whole wheat flour (gehun ka atta)
1 teaspoon (5 grams) fresh yeast, crumbled
½ teaspoon sugar
½ teaspoon salt

For the dressing
6 tablespoons low fat curds, page 153
2 cloves garlic
2 spring onions, chopped
salt to taste

For the patties
1 cup chick peas (kabuli chana), soaked overnight
1 green chilli, chopped
½ cup mint, chopped
½ teaspoon grated garlic
½ cup cabbage, grated
1 cup carrot, grated
¼ cup capsicum, finely chopped
½ teaspoon roasted cumin (jeera) powder
salt to taste
1 teaspoon oil for brushing

Other ingredients
2 tomatoes, thinly sliced
1 cup lettuce, shredded

135

For the pita bread

1 Combine all the ingredients in a bowl and using enough water, knead into a semi-soft dough until it is smooth and elastic (approx. 5 to 7 minutes).
2 Cover the dough with a wet muslin cloth and allow it to prove till it doubles in volume (approx. 15 to 20 minutes).
3 Press the dough lightly to remove the air.
4 Divide the dough into 6 equal parts.
5 Roll out each portion into a circle of 25 mm. (4") diameter and 4 mm. (1/6") thickness.
6 Cook one circle on a hot tava (griddle) on each side for a minute or until the bread puffs up.
7 Remove and keep aside. Repeat for the remaining circles to make more pita bread.
8 Cut each pita bread into 2 halves. Keep aside.

For the dressing

Blend all the ingredients in a liquidiser into a smooth sauce. Keep refrigerated.

For the patties

1 Drain the water from the chick peas.
2 Grind the chick peas, green chilli and mint in a blender to a coarse paste without using water.
3 Add the remaining ingredients and mix well.
4 Divide the mixture into 12 equal parts and shape them into patties.
5 Brush a non-stick pan with the oil and cook the patties till golden brown in colour.
6 Drain on absorbent paper and keep aside.

How to proceed

1 Warm the pita bread halves on a hot tava (griddle).
2 Fill each pita bread half with some tomato slices and shredded lettuce, one patty and a spoonful of the dressing on top.
3 Repeat for the remaining pita bread halves and other ingredients to make 11 more falafels.
   Serve immediately.

Handy tip: You can use ½ teaspoon (2.5 grams) dry yeast dissolved in lukewarm water instead of fresh yeast for the pita breads in the above recipe.

❧ Nutritive values per falafel : ❧

AMT	ENERGY	PROTEIN	CHO	FAT	VIT. A	VIT. C	CALCIUM	IRON	F.ACID	FIBRE
gm	kcal	gm	gm	gm	mcg	mg	mg	mg	mcg	gm
64	75	3.1	13.3	1.0	370.9	14.1	46.0	1.5	23.5	0.8

Exchange list per falafel :

CEREAL	PULSE	VEGETABLE	FRUIT	MILK	FAT		CEREAL	PULSE	VEGETABLE	FRUIT	MILK	FAT
¼	¼	½	–	–	¼	**OR**	½	–	½	–	–	¼

❧ Dieter's Pizza ❧

Picture on page 101

Prep. time :

30 minutes.

Cooking time :

45 minutes.

Makes 2 pizzas (8 servings).

Baking time :

20 minutes.

Baking temperature :

200°C (400°F).

Today, pizzas are easily available at every restaurant and of course with any number of variations. Here's one variation specially created for diabetics to indulge in ... *once in a while*.

The pizza base in this recipe is made using whole wheat flour (and not refined flour (maida) which has a high glycemic index and raises the blood sugar levels rapidly).

I have used a creamy mixture of mustard flavoured low fat cream cheese instead of cheese. This miracle spread not only melts well but also tastes good, of course, not like real cheese, but a good guilt free substitute.

You can use any other low fat vegetable toppings that you like instead of the one used in this recipe.

For the pizza base
2 cups whole wheat flour (gehun ka atta)
2 teaspoons (10 grams) fresh yeast, crumbled
a pinch sugar
1 teaspoon salt

For the tomato sauce
4 large tomatoes

1 small onion, chopped
1 teaspoon garlic, chopped
½ teaspoon dried oregano
1 teaspoon oil
salt to taste

For the cheesy topping
½ cup low fat paneer, page 154
2 tablespoons low fat milk, page 152
½ teaspoon french style mustard

Other ingredients
½ cup zucchini, sliced (optional)
½ cup onions, sliced
1 tomato, sliced
10 to 12 basil leaves
1 teaspoon oil for greasing

For pizza base
1 Combine all the ingredients in a bowl. Knead into a soft dough using enough water until it is smooth and elastic.
2 Cover the dough with a wet muslin cloth and allow it to prove till it doubles in volume (approx. 15 to 20 minutes).
3 Press the dough lightly to remove the air.
4 Divide the dough into 2 equal parts.
5 Roll out each portion into a circle of 250 mm. (10") diameter and 6 mm. (¼") thickness and place on a lightly greased baking tray.

For the tomato sauce
1 Blanch the tomatoes in boiling water.
2 Peel, cut into quarters and deseed the tomatoes. Chop finely and keep aside the tomato pulp.
3 Heat the oil, add the onion and garlic and sauté for a few minutes.
4 Add the tomato pulp and allow to simmer for 10 to 15 minutes until the sauce reduces a little.
5 Add salt and simmer for some more time.
Finally, add the oregano and mix well. Keep aside.

For the cheesy topping
Blend the paneer, milk and mustard to a smooth purée in a liquidiser and keep aside.

How to proceed
1 Spread half the tomato sauce over the pizza base and top with the cheesy topping mixture.
2 Arrange half the zucchini, onion and tomato slices on the pizza and top with some basil leaves.
3 Bake in a pre-heated oven at 200°C (400°F) for 10 to 15 minutes or till the base is evenly browned. Top with some more basil leaves.
4 Make another pizza using the other pizza base and the remaining ingredients.
   Divide each pizza into 4 pieces and serve hot.

❧ Nutritive values per pizza : ❧

AMT	ENERGY	PROTEIN	CHO	FAT	VIT. A	VIT. C	CALCIUM	IRON	F.ACID	FIBRE
gm	kcal	gm	gm	gm	mcg	mg	mg	mg	mcg	gm
84	139	6.2	24.6	1.8	157.1	11.8	121.5	1.8	21.9	0.9

Exchange list per pizza :

CEREAL	PULSE	VEGETABLE	FRUIT	MILK	FAT
½	–	1	–	½	¼

Spicy Vegetable Risotto

Prep. time :
10 minutes.

Cooking time :
20 minutes.

Serves 4.

The Italians make risotto with a special variety of rice that is called arborio. I have used bulgur wheat as a substitute for rice in this recipe to enrich this delicacy with fibre to help control blood sugar levels after a hearty and satisfying meal. The colourful veggies in this dish makes them extremely appealing and also irresistible due to their aromatic flavours while being cooked.

This risotto is a storehouse of nutrients like protein, vitamin A, vitamin C, iron, calcium as well as fibre. Cook this dish as close to the serving time as possible, as it is best when freshly prepared.

1 cup bulgur wheat (dalia)
1 onion, finely chopped
½ cup red and green capsicum, diced
½ cup mushrooms, sliced
½ cup brinjals (baingan), diced
½ cup zucchini, diced (optional)
½ cup green peas
¼ cup carrots, diced
1 cup low fat milk, page 152
1 tablespoon grated cheese
½ teaspoon mixed dried herbs
1 teaspoon olive oil or oil
salt to taste

To be ground into a chilli-garlic paste
2 cloves garlic
2 whole red chillies

1 Clean, wash and soak the bulgur wheat. Drain the water and keep aside.
2 Heat the olive oil in a non-stick pan and sauté the onion pieces till they are translucent.
3 Add the capsicum, mushroom, brinjals, zucchini, peas, carrots and chilli-garlic paste and sauté for 2 to 3 minutes.
4 Add the bulgur wheat, water and salt and cook till all the water is absorbed.

5 Add the milk, cheese and dried herbs and allow to simmer for some more time.
Serve hot.

❧ Nutritive values per serving : ❧

AMT	ENERGY	PROTEIN	CHO	FAT	VIT. A	VIT. C	CALCIUM	IRON	F.ACID	FIBRE
gm	kcal	gm	gm	gm	mcg	mg	mg	mg	mcg	gm
124	205	7.6	38.1	2.6	174.8	27.0	119.5	2.6	10.2	1.9

Exchange list per serving :

CEREAL	PULSE	VEGETABLE	FRUIT	MILK	FAT
1	—	2	—	½	¼

Desserts

❧ Shrikhand ❧

Prep. time :

5 minutes.

No Cooking.

Serves 4.

This creamy delicacy is made with all the goodness of milk without the fat since we have used hung low fat curds. Use fresh curds for best results.

You can also add strawberries or pineapples instead of the saffron and cardamom to make a fruit flavoured shrikhand.

1 cup hung low fat curds, page 153
½ teaspoon cardamom (elaichi) powder
a few saffron strands
2 tablespoons low fat milk, page 152
4 sachets sugar substitute

1   Combine all the ingredients and mix well.
2   Chill for at least 2 to 3 hours.
    Serve chilled.

Handy tip : Approx. 2 cups fresh curds will give you 1 cup hung curds. You have to hang the curds in a thin muslin cloth for approx. 25 minutes.

❧ Nutritive values per serving : ❧

AMT	ENERGY	PROTEIN	CHO	FAT	VIT. A	VIT. C	CALCIUM	IRON	F.ACID	FIBRE
gm	kcal	gm	gm	gm	mcg	mg	mg	mg	mcg	gm
11	40	4.1	5.7	0.0	0.0	0.5	147.9	0.2	0.0	0.1

Exchange list per serving :

CEREAL	PULSE	VEGETABLE	FRUIT	MILK	FAT
–	–	–	–	½	–

❦ Malai Peda ❦

Picture on page 102

Prep. time :

25 minutes.

Cooking time :

50 minutes.

Makes 7 pedas.

These soft pedas with a grainy texture are an all-time favourite. So here's a healthy recipe made with low fat milk for diabetics to relish. The use of milk makes these pedas rich in protein and calcium. A teaspoon of cornflour has been added as a binding agent. Saffron adds a delightful colour to the pedas and makes them all the more irresistible.

1 litre low fat milk, page 152
a few saffron strands
¼ teaspoon citric acid
2 level teaspoons cornflour
½ teaspoon cardamom (elaichi) powder
4 sachets sugar substitute

For the garnish
1 teaspoon pistachios, chopped (optional) or a few saffron strands

1 Keep 4 teaspoons of milk aside and boil the remaining milk in a heavy bottomed pan, stirring throughout, until it reduces to half.

2 Warm the saffron in a small vessel, add 4 teaspoons of milk and rub until the saffron dissolves. Add to the boiling milk.

3 Mix the citric acid in 3 teaspoons of water. Add this mixture very gradually to the boiling milk until it curdles slightly. This may require anything from half to the entire quantity of the citric acid mixture.

4 Mix the cornflour in 4 teaspoons of water and add to the boiling mixture.

5 Continue stirring till the mixture becomes thick and resembles khoya. Add the cardamom powder and mix well. Allow to cool. Add the sugar substitute and mix well.

6 Shape into 7 small balls and serve, garnished saffron or pistachio.

AMT	ENERGY	PROTEIN	CHO	FAT	VIT. A	VIT. C	CALCIUM	IRON	F.ACID	FIBRE
gm	kcal	gm	gm	gm	mcg	mg	mg	mg	mcg	gm
5	14	1.4	2.2	0.0	0.5	0.3	47.3	0.1	0.0	0.1

Exchange list per peda :

CEREAL	PULSE	VEGETABLE	FRUIT	MILK	FAT
–	–	–	–	¼	–

Apple Rabadi

Prep. time :

10 minutes.

Cooking time :

25 minutes.

Serves 4.

Low fat milk thickened with apple. The addition of nutmeg and cardamom blends well with the subtle flavours. Try not to peel the apple, as much of the fibre is present in the peel and just below it.

Select sweet apples for this recipe, as sharp apples can split the rabadi and render it useless.

3 cups low fat milk, page 152
1 cup apple, grated
a pinch nutmeg (jaiphal) powder
¼ teaspoon cardamom (elaichi) powder
2 sachets sugar substitute

1 Bring the milk to boil in a heavy bottomed pan and simmer it for 10 to 12 minutes.
2 Add the grated apple, nutmeg powder and cardamom powder and simmer for another 5 to 7 minutes.
3 Cool completely. Add the sugar substitute, mix well and put to chill. Serve chilled.

AMT	ENERGY	PROTEIN	CHO	FAT	VIT. A	VIT. C	CALCIUM	IRON	F.ACID	FIBRE
gm	kcal	gm	gm	gm	mcg	mg	mg	mg	mcg	gm
37	67	5.8	10.7	0.1	0.0	1.0	207.9	0.4	0.0	0.2

Exchange list per serving :

CEREAL	PULSE	VEGETABLE	FRUIT	MILK	FAT
—	—	—	½	½	—

Lemon Cheesecake

picture on page 57

Prep. time :

15 minutes.

Cooking time :

15 minutes.

Serves 4.

Setting time :

1 hour.

This summery cheesecake is wonderful if you are looking for a dessert to be prepared well in advance.
The digestive biscuits, bound with a little bit of butter, give a light and crispy texture to the crust.
The cheesecake mixture is flavoured with lemon juice and zest that lends its characteristic freshness to this dessert, while the sugar substitute provides the necessary sweetness.

For the crust
10 digestive biscuits, crushed
2 teaspoons low fat butter, melted

For the cheesecake mixture
1 recipe low fat cream cheese, page 158
½ cup low fat curds, page 153
4 sachets sugar substitute
1 teaspoon lemon juice
1 teaspoon lemon zest
a few drops lemon essence

For the topping (optional)
2 tablespoons sugarfree orange marmalade

For the crust

1 Combine the butter and biscuits and line the bottom of a 100 mm. (4") diameter loose bottomed cake tin.
2 Refrigerate till set.

For the cheesecake mixture

1 Blend the cream cheese in a blender till it is smooth and free of lumps, adding some warm milk or whey if required.
2 Combine with the remaining ingredients in a bowl and whisk till it is a smooth mixture.

For the topping

1 Combine the marmalade with 1 tablespoon of water in a pan and melt over gentle heat. Cool slightly.

How to proceed

1 Pour the cheesecake mixture over the set crust and refrigerate till the mixture sets.
2 Pour the warm topping over and chill again for 10 to 15 minutes.
3 Cut into wedges and serve cold.

❧ Nutritive values per serving : ❧

AMT	ENERGY	PROTEIN	CHO	FAT	VIT. A	VIT. C	CALCIUM	IRON	F.ACID	FIBRE
gm	kcal	gm	gm	gm	mcg	mg	mg	mg	mcg	gm
36	145	8.1	19.3	3.9	0.0	1.7	255.2	0.6	0.0	0.0

Exchange list per serving :

CEREAL	PULSE	VEGETABLE	FRUIT	MILK	FAT
–	–	–	1	¾	½

Diabetic Caramel Custard

Picture on page 128

Prep. time :

60 minutes (1 hour).

Cooking time :

15 minutes.

Serves 4.

A light and tasty pudding not only for diabetics but for all those who are health conscious and want to avoid sugar laden desserts.

The low fat milk used in this recipe has a wealth of nutrients like protein and calcium which is extremely essential for the maintenance of healthy bones.

I have used one teaspoon of sugar to make the caramel, but you can avoid it and simply enjoy the custard.

2½ cups low fat milk, page 152
1 tablespoon custard powder
3 sachets sugar substitute
½ teaspoon vanilla essence
5 grams China grass (agar agar), cut into small pieces
1 teaspoon sugar for caramelising

1 Soak the China grass in ¾ cup of cold water for 15 to 20 minutes. Put to cook on a slow flame until it dissolves. Keep warm.
2 In a pudding mould, add the sugar (for caramelising) and 1 teaspoon of water and continue cooking until the sugar becomes brown. Spread the caramelised sugar all over the base of the mould, rotating the mould to spread it evenly. The sugar will harden quickly.
3 Mix the custard powder in ½ cup of cold milk.
4 Boil the remaining milk. When it comes to a boil, add the custard powder and milk mixture and continue cooking till you get a smooth sauce.
5 Add the China grass solution to the custard and boil again for 2 minutes.
6 Strain the mixture and cool it slightly. (Strain the mixture if it is lumpy).
7 Add the vanilla essence and sugar substitute and mix well. Pour this mixture over the prepared pudding mould. Allow to set in a refrigerator.
8 Before serving, loosen the sides with a sharp knife and invert on a plate. Serve chilled.

Handy tip : The mould should be approx. 125 mm. (5") in diameter to get a 50 mm. (2") high custard.

AMT	ENERGY	PROTEIN	CHO	FAT	VIT. A	VIT. C	CALCIUM	IRON	F.ACID	FIBRE
gm	kcal	gm	gm	gm	mcg	mg	mg	mg	mcg	gm
14	49	4.8	7.5	0.0	0.0	0.6	171.3	0.2	0.0	0.0

Exchange list per serving :

CEREAL	PULSE	VEGETABLE	FRUIT	MILK	FAT
–	–	–	–	½	–

Sugarfree Stawberry Ice-Cream

Prep. time :

20 minutes.

Cooking time :

10 minutes.

Serves 4.

Relish this delicious ice-cream when fresh strawberries are in season. This rich, creamy, ice-cream is made with reduced milk, thickened with cornflour and sweetened with a sugar substitute. You will need to add less sugar substitute if the fruit you use is ripe and sweet. Taste the ice-cream mixture after you add and mix each sachet to ascertain how much you need to add.

Fresh lychees or kala jamun can also be used as an alternative to strawberries.

2½ cups (½ litre) low fat milk, page 152
2 tablespoons cornflour
1 cup fresh strawberries, chopped
3 to 4 sachets sugar substitute

1   Mix the cornflour in ½ cup of cold milk and keep aside.
2   Bring the remaining milk to a boil in a non-stick pan and add the cornflour mixture.
3   Stir continuously and simmer over a slow flame till it coats the back of a spoon.
4   Cool completely. Add the sugar substitute and the strawberries and pour into an air-tight container.
5   Freeze for 4 to 6 hours.
6   Liquidise in a blender till it is slushy and pour back into the air-tight container. Freeze till the ice-cream is set.

AMT	ENERGY	PROTEIN	CHO	FAT	VIT. A	VIT. C	CALCIUM	IRON	F.ACID	FIBRE
gm	kcal	gm	gm	gm	mcg	mg	mg	mg	mcg	gm
58	71	5.4	11.9	0.2	9.2	20.6	183.2	0.9	0.0	0.6

Exchange list per serving :

CEREAL	PULSE	VEGETABLE	FRUIT	MILK	FAT
—	—	—	—	½	—

Stuffed Lychees

Prep. time :

10 minutes.

Cooking time :

10 minutes.

Makes 15 pieces.

These dainty chenna filled lychees are sure to melt in your mouth. Choose sweet lychees to make this dessert because sharp or acidic lychees are not going to complement the filling. You can have 2 pieces at one time without feeling guilty.

15 fresh lychees, peeled

To be blended into a filling
½ cup low fat paneer, page 154
2 tablespoons low fat milk, page 152
2 sachets sugar substitute
½ teaspoon vanilla essence

1 Carefully deseed the lychees.
2 Stuff each deseeded lychee with a teaspoon of the filling. Refrigerate for 30 minutes.
Serve chilled.

Nutritive values per piece :

AMT	ENERGY	PROTEIN	CHO	FAT	VIT. A	VIT. C	CALCIUM	IRON	F.ACID	FIBRE
gm	kcal	gm	gm	gm	mcg	mg	mg	mg	mcg	gm
18	21	1.4	3.7	0.0	0.0	4.8	46.3	0.2	0.0	0.1

CEREAL	PULSE	VEGETABLE	FRUIT	MILK	FAT		CEREAL	PULSE	VEGETABLE	FRUIT	MILK	FAT
–	–	–	½	–	–	OR	–	–	–	–	¼	–

❦ Orange Rum Cake ❧

Prep. time :

10 minutes.

Serves 6.

Baking time :

25 minutes.

Baking temperature :

200°C (400°F).

This delightful orange and rum flavoured cake is one that will melt in your mouth. The butter used in this recipe is relatively low in fat and carbohydrates and so is suitable for a diabetic diet. You can skip the rum if you wish and simply add 2 tablespoons of fat free milk or water instead.

However remember that moderation is the key here and it is wise to restrict these treats to occasional indulgences.

1 cup whole wheat flour (gehun ka atta)
½ teaspoon baking powder
½ cup low fat butter, softened
8 sachets sugar substitute
¼ cup orange juice
½ cup buttermilk (made from 2½ tablespoons low fat curds, page 153)
1 teaspoon orange rind
2 tablespoons rum

1 Sieve the wheat flour and baking powder together and keep aside.
2 Combine the butter and sugar substitute in a bowl and beat till the mixture is smooth and creamy.
3 Add the orange juice, buttermilk, orange rind, rum and wheat flour mixture and mix well.
4 Pour the batter into a 125 mm. (5") diameter greased cake tin.
5 Bake in a pre-heated oven at 200°C (400°F) for 20 to 25 minutes.
6 Cut into 6 wedges.

AMT	ENERGY	PROTEIN	CHO	FAT	VIT. A	VIT. C	CALCIUM	IRON	F.ACID	FIBRE
gm	kcal	gm	gm	gm	mcg	mg	mg	mg	mcg	gm
40	159	3.7	14.8	8.7	6.3	4.5	17.6	0.9	6.4	0.3

Exchange list per serving :

CEREAL	PULSE	VEGETABLE	FRUIT	MILK	FAT
¼	—	—	1	½	1

BASIC RECIPES

≈ Low Fat Milk ≈

Prep. time :

5 minutes.

Cooking time :

7 minutes.

Makes I litre (5 cups).

This low fat milk has been made using skim milk powder and is virtually fat free while having all the goodness of milk like protein, calcium and vitamin B_2. Skim milk powder is easily available at all leading grocery stores. Alternatively, feel free to use 99% fat free milk (low fat milk) readily available in tetrapacks at most grocery stores.

Refer to page 28, for the homemade version of Low Fat Milk .

100 grams skim milk powder
1 litre water

1 Mix the skim milk powder in 1½ cups of water and make a smooth paste.
2 Add the remaining water and if desired, mix with a whisk.
3 Boil and use as required.

≈ Nutritive values per cup : ≈

AMT	ENERGY	PROTEIN	CHO	FAT	VIT. A	VIT. C	CALCIUM	IRON	F.ACID	FIBRE
ml	kcal	gm	gm	gm	mcg	mg	mg	mg	mcg	gm
200	71	7.6	10.2	0.0	0.0	1.0	274.0	0.3	0.0	0.0

～ Low Fat Curds ～

Prep. time :

5 minutes.

Setting time :

4 hours.

Makes 5 cups.

Curds are a nutritious addition to the diet. They are easier to digest than milk. Curds complement the protein present in cereals and make it a complete protein, when accompanied by dishes like parathas, biryanis etc.

Use this low fat version of curds as an accompaniment to a main meal or in raitas, salad dressings etc. to enjoy all the goodness of curds without the fat.

1 litre low fat milk, page 152
1 tablespoon curds (made the previous day)

1 Warm the milk, till it is just about lukewarm.
2 Add the curds, mix well and cover.
3 Keep aside until the curds set (approx. 5 to 6 hours). During the cold climate, place inside a casserole or closed oven to set.

Handy tip : Curd set quickly in a warm and dark place.

～ Nutritive values per cup : ～

AMT	ENERGY	PROTEIN	CHO	FAT	VIT. A	VIT. C	CALCIUM	IRON	F.ACID	FIBRE
ml	kcal	gm	gm	gm	mcg	mg	mg	mg	mcg	gm
200	71	7.6	10.2	0.0	0.0	1.0	274.0	0.3	0.0	0.0

Low Fat Paneer

Prep. time :

30 minutes.

Cooking time :

10 minutes.

Makes 100 grams.

(approx. ¾ cup).

This paneer is made using skim milk that has all the goodness of milk without the fat. For milk fussy adults, this is a superb way of adding protein (necessary for maintenance of body cells) and calcium (necessary for healthy bones) to the diet.

2 cups low fat milk, page 152
1 cup low fat curds, page 153, beaten

1 Put the milk to boil in a broad pan. When it starts boiling, add the low fat curds and mix well.
2 Remove from the heat and stir gently until the milk curdles.
3 Strain and tie the curdled milk in a muslin cloth. Hang for about half an hour to allow the whey to drain out.
   Use as required.

Note : If the milk has not curdled completely at step 2, allow the milk to boil once more.

Handy tip : If you want firm paneer, cover the block with a heavy weight to compress the paneer. This way you will be able to cut cubes from the paneer.

⤳ Nutritive values for 100 grams (¾ cup): ⤶

AMT	ENERGY	PROTEIN	CHO	FAT	VIT. A	VIT. C	CALCIUM	IRON	F.ACID	FIBRE
gm	kcal	gm	gm	gm	mcg	mg	mg	mg	mcg	gm
100	214	22.8	30.6	0.1	0.0	3.0	822.0	0.8	0.0	0.0

Clear Vegetable Stock

Prep. time :

5 minutes.

Cooking time :

20 minutes.

Makes 5 cups.

A lot of vegetables are used to prepare this flavourful stock. These vegetables have a wealth of nutrients that are released into the water and are retained by the stock. The stock retains all the water-soluble vitamins like vitamins B and C that are many times lost during cooking.

Use this stock in soups and gravies to enhance their flavours.

⅓ cup cabbage, roughly chopped
3 carrots, roughly chopped
5 to 6 celery stalks
2 tablespoons chopped spring onions (including greens)
3 to 4 pieces cauliflower

1 Boil the vegetables in 6 cups of water on a medium flame for 15 to 20 minutes.
2 Allow the vegetables to settle at the bottom of the vessel and pour out the vegetable stock. Discard the vegetables and use as required.

Nutritive values per cup :

AMT	ENERGY	PROTEIN	CHO	FAT	VIT. A	VIT. C	CALCIUM	IRON	F.ACID	FIBRE
gm	kcal	gm	gm	gm	mcg	mg	mg	mg	mcg	gm
74	32	0.7	6.9	0.1	1178.4	9.8	67.2	1.0	10.2	0.9

❧ Corn Tortillas ❧

Prep. time :

15 minutes.

Cooking time :

5 minutes.

Makes 12 tortillas.

Tortillas are the bread of Mexico, similar to our chapatis, being flat, round and unleavened. These keep well for a few days if refrigerated and can be used to make quesidillas, Burritos, page 122.

The combination of whole wheat and maize flour is a protein packed one. I have used warm water to knead the dough as it yields a softer dough that is easier to roll and also makes softer tortillas.

1¼ cups maize flour (makai ka atta)
¾ cup wheat flour (gehun ka atta)
3 teaspoons oil
¾ teaspoon salt

1 Mix the flours, oil and salt and make a dough by adding enough warm water.
2 Knead the dough well and keep aside for 30 minutes. Knead again.
3 Divide the dough into 12 equal parts and roll out each portion into rounds of 100 mm. to 125 mm. (4" to 5") diameter.
4 Cook each round lightly on a tava (griddle) and keep aside.

Handy tip : As tortillas are used extensively in Mexican food, you can make large quantities and freeze in a refrigerator.

❧ Nutritive values per tortilla : ❧

AMT	ENERGY	PROTEIN	CHO	FAT	VIT. A	VIT. C	CALCIUM	IRON	F.ACID	FIBRE
gm	kcal	gm	gm	gm	mcg	mg	mg	mg	mcg	gm
18	47	1.3	7.1	1.5	16.4	0.6	4.1	0.4	2.4	0.3

~ Refried Beans ~

Prep. time :

15 minutes.

Cooking time :

25 minutes.

Makes I cup.

Mexico's famous beans aren't really "refried" at all. Re in Spanish means "thoroughly cooked" i.e. the beans are almost overcooked till they resemble a purée like consistency.

This hearty dish appears on Mexican tables at every meal from breakfast to midnight, as beans are economical, delicious and nourishing. They keep well when refrigerated and can be used to make a meal when accompanied by tortillas or even as a sandwich filling to make a grilled whole wheat sandwich.

Use these beans in recipes like Burritos, page 122.

¼ cup kidney beans (rajma), soaked overnight
a pinch soda bi-carb
2 large cloves garlic, finely chopped
1 onion, finely chopped
1 cup tomatoes, chopped
¼ cup capsicum, finely chopped
1 teaspoon chilli powder
1 teaspoon roasted cumin seed (jeera) powder
1 teaspoon oil
salt to taste

1 Pressure cook the kidney beans, salt and soda bi-carb till the beans are soft and slightly overcooked.
2 Drain the beans and grind to a coarse paste in a blender.
3 Heat the oil in a non-stick pan, add the garlic and onion and sauté till the onion turns translucent.
4 Add the tomatoes and sauté for another 3 to 4 minutes.
5 Add the ground beans, capsicum, chilli powder, cumin seed powder and salt mix well. Cook for 5 minutes. Add water if required to adjust the consistency.

Use as required.

～ Nutritive values per cup : ～

AMT	ENERGY	PROTEIN	CHO	FAT	VIT. A	VIT. C	CALCIUM	IRON	F.ACID	FIBRE
gm	kcal	gm	gm	gm	mcg	mg	mg	mg	mcg	gm
277	165	5.6	22.8	5.6	724.9	92.5	145.5	2.3	51.1	2.6

Low Fat Cream Cheese

Prep. time :

a few minutes.

Cooking time :

10 minutes.

Makes approx. I cup.

Cream cheese is a type of cheese spread available abroad in most supermarkets. Since it is not very easily available in India, I have made it using fresh low fat milk. Being made from low fat milk, this cream cheese is absolutely fat free and can be relished without any guilt even by diabetics with high cholesterol levels.

Use this cream cheese to make delectable desserts (as I have done in the recipe of Lemon Cheesecake, page 146) or even to make delectable dips to serve at parties along with vegetable crudites.

1 litre low fat milk, page 152
1 teaspoon citric acid crystals
½ cup warm water

1 Put the milk to boil in a thick bottomed pan.
2 When it comes to a boil, remove from the flame and keep aside for a few minutes.
3 In another bowl, mix the citric acid crystals with the warm water.
4 Pour this mixture into the hot milk and allow it to stand for about 5 minutes till the milk curdles on its own. Stir gently if required.
5 Strain this mixture using a muslin cloth, leaving some of the whey in the curdled mixture.
6 Blend the drained milk solids in a food processor till it is thick and creamy. Use as required.

Handy tips : **1)** If the drained whey is milky, boil it once more and strain the separated milk solids.
2) You can also use ½ tablespoon of lemon juice instead of the citric acid Crystals.

Nutritive values per cup :

AMT	ENERGY	PROTEIN	CHO	FAT	VIT. A	VIT. C	CALCIUM	IRON	F.ACID	FIBRE
gm	kcal	gm	gm	gm	mcg	mg	mg	mg	mcg	gm
144	357	38.0	51.0	0.1	0.0	5.0	1370.0	1.4	0.0	0.0

Sample Diabetic Menu Plans

1st Menu

MEAL	TIME	MENU	AMOUNT	ENERGY (kcal)	PROTEIN (gm)	CHO (gm)	FAT (gm)	FIBRE (gm)
Breakfast	8.00 am	Whole Wheat Corn Flake Rolls, page 100	2 nos.	262	8.8	47.6	4.0	2.2
		Hummus, page 98	3 tbsps.	114	5.4	18.3	2.4	1.2
		Carrot	1 medium	48	0.9	10.6	0.2	1.2
				424	15.1	76.5	6.6	4.6
Mid Morning	10.00 am	Karela Muthias, page 83	1 serving	105	4.1	17.4	2.1	3.7
		Carrot Garlic Chutney, page 86	1 tbsp.	13	0.1	1.4	0.7	0.2
				118	4.2	18.8	2.8	3.9
Pre Lunch	12.00 pm	Sweet Corn and Spring Onion Soup, page 110	2 servings	104	3.4	16.4	3.0	2.0
				104	3.4	16.4	3.0	2.0
Lunch	2.00 pm	Paneer Khulchas, page 60	2 nos.	236	12.6	40.2	2.8	0.8
		Khumb Hara Dhania, page 69	1 serving	60	4.1	8.0	1.5	0.6
		Apple	1 medium	124	0.4	28.1	1.1	2.1
				420	17.1	76.3	5.4	3.5
Post Lunch	4.00 pm	Orange Tabbouleh, page 117	½ serving	101	2.0	19.5	1.7	0.7
				101	2.0	19.5	1.7	0.7
Mid Eve.	6.00 pm	Burritos, page 122	1 no.	104	5.1	15.3	2.4	0.8
				104	5.1	15.3	2.4	0.8
Dinner	8.00 pm	Chinese Fried Rice, page 125	1 serving	177	3.5	35.8	2.2	0.8
		Hot and Sour Vegetables, page 129	1 serving	46	1.3	7.1	1.5	0.8
		Hakka Mushrooms, page 95	2 servings	62	3.2	76	2.8	1.6
		Lemon Cheesecake, page 146	1 serving	145	8.1	69.8	10.4	3.2
				430	16.1	69.8	10.4	3.2
Bed Time	10.00 pm	Low Fat Milk, page 152	1 cup	71	7.6	6.8	1.8	1.3
	Total			1740	67.2	298.7	32.5	21.1

159

~2nd Menu~

MEAL	TIME	MENU	AMOUNT	ENERGY (kcal)	PROTEIN (gm)	CHO (gm)	FAT (gm)	FIBRE (gm)
Breakfast	8.00 am	Varagu.Upma, page 81	1 serving	176	6.1	31.5	3.1	4.3
		Apple	1 large (approx. 250 gm)	148	0.5	33.5	1.3	2.3
		Low Fat Milk, page 152	1 cup	71	7.6	6.8	1.8	1.3
				395	**14.2**	**71.8**	**6.2**	**7.9**
Pre Lunch	11.00 am	Digestive Biscuits	4 nos.	174	2.5	23.0	7.9	0.0
				174	**2.5**	**23.0**	**7.9**	**0.0**
Lunch	2.00 pm	Phulka	2 nos.	102	3.6	20.8	8.5	0.6
		Stuffed Karelas in Makhani Gravy, page 63	1 serving	135	7.7	20.7	2.4	1.4
		Moong and Buckwheat Khichdi, page 74	½ serving	124	5.1	22.7	1.4	2.4
		Burnt Corn Salad, page 112	1 serving	67	2.1	10.9	1.7	1.2
				428	**18.5**	**75.1**	**6.0**	**5.6**
Snacks	5.00 pm	Quick Soya Dosas, page 87	1 no.	140	5.6	24.1	2.3	0.3
		Low Calorie Green Chutney, page 85	1 tbsp.	46	2.5	7.2	0.8	0.2
				186	**8.1**	**31.3**	**3.1**	**0.5**
Dinner	8.00 pm	Nourishing Barley Soup, page 107	1 serving	51	2.0	7.8	1.4	0.6
		Moussaka, page 132	2 servings	198	6.7	24.4	8.5	3.2
		Spring Salad, page 118	1½ servings	175	8.9	28.2	3.0	2.2
		Black Jamun, chopped	½ cup	62	0.7	14.0	0.3	0.2
				486	**18.3**	**74.4**	**13.2**	**6.2**
Bed Time	10.00 pm	Low Fat Milk, page 152	1 cup	**71**	**7.6**	**6.8**	**1.8**	**1.3**
		Total		**1740**	**69.2**	**282.4**	**38.2**	**21.5**